Family-Based Treatment for Eating Disorders Piece by Piece

This book illustrates how parents who are participating in family-based treatment (FBT) for their child's eating disorder (ED) may enhance their chances of achieving optimal outcomes for their child by more successfully navigating the challenges that often impede progress in treatment and recovery.

The stance of this book is transdiagnostic, so that the information provided spans all ED diagnoses including anorexia nervosa, bulimia nervosa, binge eating disorder, avoidant/restrictive food intake disorder, and atypical ED presentations as well as conditions that fall outside current diagnostic criteria. This book helps parents to identify how they can make the most of FBT therapy no matter which ED symptoms their child experiences. Case vignettes across the diagnostic and clinical spectrum are used throughout the book, not only to illustrate examples of some specific challenges families face, but to help parents normalize the emotions they may feel around their experience of trying to help their child and around their experience of participating in the FBT intervention itself.

James Lock, MD, PhD is the Eric Rothenberg, MD professor of psychiatry and pediatrics at Stanford University School of Medicine. He is an internationally recognized expert in the treatment of eating disorders in children and youth and one of the original developers of family-based treatment.

Aileen Whyte, PhD is a clinical associate professor at Stanford University School of Medicine where she also serves as director of the Stanford Outpatient Child & Adolescent Eating Disorders Clinic. Dr. Whyte has significant experience in the provision of FBT to young people with eating disorders. Dr. Whyte has led multiple seminars and workshops in the treatment of eating disorders and provides ongoing supervision and consultation in the FBT approach.

Brittany Matheson, PhD is a licensed clinical psychologist in the Department of Psychiatry and Behavioral Sciences at Stanford University School of Medicine. Dr. Matheson is a certified FBT provider engaged in patient care, research efforts, and supervision of postdoctoral and psychiatry trainees and fellows.

Nandini Datta, PhD is a clinical instructor/faculty scholar at Stanford University School of Medicine. Dr. Datta is a certified FBT provider and has experience working with eating disorders across both outpatient and inpatient settings. She is also engaged in ongoing research trials using FBT from both a supervisory and a clinical standpoint.

Family-Based Treatment for Eating Disorders Piece by Piece

A Practical Guide for Parents

James Lock, Aileen Whyte, Brittany Matheson, and Nandini Datta

With illustrations by Nandini Datta

Routledge
Taylor & Francis Group

NEW YORK AND LONDON

First published 2024
by Routledge
605 Third Avenue, New York, NY 10158

and by Routledge
4 Park Square, Milton Park, Abingdon, Oxon, OX14 4RN

Routledge is an imprint of the Taylor & Francis Group, an informa business

ISBN: 9781032404318 (hbk)
ISBN: 9781032404295 (pbk)
ISBN: 9781003353041 (ebk)

DOI: 10.4324/9781003353041

Typeset in Goudy
by Newgen Publishing UK

This book is dedicated to the many parents and families who have helped us learn what will help them to be successful in helping their children with eating disorders. We would also like to dedicate this book to our own families who have supported us in our work.

Contents

Preface

This book is for parents who are receiving treatment for their children with eating disorders using Family-Based Treatment (FBT). There is compelling data that FBT is effective for adolescents with Anorexia Nervosa (AN) and Bulimia Nervosa (BN) as well as support that FBT reduces binge eating and is likely helpful for Avoidant/Restrictive Food Intake Disorder (ARFID) in younger children. FBT encourages parents and families as a whole to find ways to disrupt and manage the eating disorder symptoms that undermine the emotional and physical health of their children. Therapists in FBT support parents in determining the best ways this can be accomplished in each unique family. Therapists help parents think through and evaluate decisions rather than direct them about what should be done.

Sometimes parents struggle in FBT—helping a child with an eating disorder is hard work—so this is not surprising. Over their many years of providing FBT, the clinicians who have authored this book have identified some common dilemmas parents face in FBT. This book is meant to help parents anticipate these problems while also suggesting ways that might help parents overcome them. The book can be read from front to back or any chapter (except the Introduction and Conclusion) can be read on its own if parents want information about the topic covered in a specific chapter. That said, many of the common obstacles parents face do inter-relate so reading the book in its entirety will be helpful for most parents.

Introduction

This book is intended to be a helpful resource for parents who are participating in Family-Based Treatment (FBT) for their child's eating disorder (ED). The book describes how parents who are participating in FBT may enhance their chances of achieving optimal outcomes for their child by more successfully navigating the challenges that often impede progress in treatment and recovery. Each chapter describes a specific common challenge that parents face when participating in FBT for their child's ED, identifies how the challenge prevents parents from making effective progress, and makes suggestions for how they might intervene more effectively to help their child recover. Each chapter also includes relevant clinical vignettes to further illustrate navigation of these challenges.

The stance of the book is transdiagnostic, so that the information provided spans all ED diagnoses including Anorexia Nervosa (AN), Bulimia Nervosa (BN), Binge Eating Disorder (BED), Avoidant/Restrictive Food Intake Disorder (ARFID), and Atypical ED presentations as well as conditions that fall just outside current ED diagnostic criteria. For cases of AN and low weight ARFID, the initial focus of parental intervention will generally be around nourishment efforts, as the child will need to gain or regain lost weight. For other EDs, such as BN, BED, or Atypical Anorexia, the initial parental focus will be more about intervening to prevent the young person from engaging in harmful ED behaviors such as dietary restriction, binge eating, purging, over-exercise, or use of diet pills or laxatives. For other presentations of ARFID without low weight, the initial focus will be on decreasing fears around eating, and/or increasing range and types of foods to be eaten. Regardless of which of these is the primary problem the young person is experiencing, FBT therapy supports parents in intervening effectively to help their child. This book aims to help parents identify how they can make the most out of FBT therapy no matter which ED symptoms their child experiences.

DOI: 10.4324/9781003353041-1

Case vignettes across the diagnostic and clinical spectrum are used liberally throughout the book, not only to illustrate examples of some of the specific challenges families face, but also to help parents normalize the emotions they may feel around their experience of trying to help their child and around their experience of participating in the FBT intervention itself.

The intended audience for this book is parents who are participating in FBT for their child with an ED, but it also will be useful to psychologists, psychiatrists, social workers, and allied health practitioners who deliver FBT to young people and families.

Background and Rationale for a Book on FBT for Parents

Family-Based Treatment (FBT) for eating disorders (EDs) is the treatment with the most evidence base for EDs occurring in adolescence and it is recommended as the first-line treatment for adolescents with AN and BN. FBT leads to a recovery rate ranging between 33% and 50% by the end of treatment, with an additional 30% to 40% experiencing significant clinical improvements. FBT holds a positive, non-blaming view of families, and firmly adopts an *agnostic view of causation*. The stance of the therapist *is consultative* and *non-authoritarian*, where the therapist aims to join with and support the parents in their efforts to help their child. FBT makes use of techniques including:

1. increasing the family's understanding that the ED beliefs and behaviors are different to their child's true, healthy wishes and that the ED is a disruption of normal child and adolescent development processes (*externalization of the eating disorder*);
2. supporting and encouraging parents to take charge of the process of re-nourishing their child and/or preventing harmful ED behaviors such as restricting, binge eating, purging, over-exercise or the use of diet pills or laxatives (*parental empowerment*); and
3. an initial intense therapeutic focus on changing eating behaviors in order to successfully restore the child to health (*initial focus on intervening with ED behaviors*).

All sessions in the first phase of FBT are focused on parents taking charge and changing their child's eating behaviors, and early sessions include a family meal that allows the therapist to observe and consult directly about mealtime behaviors. In the second phase, the focus of treatment moves

Table 0.1 FBT Fundamental Assumptions

FBT Key Concepts
Agnostic as to the cause of ED—does not blame the parent or child for the disorder
Empowerment—endeavors to improve self-efficacy in parents related to changing maintaining behaviors of ED
Non-authoritarian therapeutic stance—therapist joins the family in helping them disrupt maintaining behaviors of ED
Externalization—ED is seen as an illness that is disrupting child and adolescent developmental processes
Focus on symptoms—therapy focuses on supporting parents' efforts to intervene against restriction, over-exercise, binge eating, purging, use of diet pills or laxatives, or any other behaviors that maintain ED
Uses system, strategic, narrative, and structural family therapy techniques
Focus is primarily on the therapeutic relationship with the parents, with the relationship with the patient taking a secondary role early in treatment at the start of treatment
Rapid behavioral change early in treatment is important for long-term response

to supporting the young person to regain age-appropriate independence around managing their eating, consistent with the changes the parents have employed in phase 1. Phase 3 is only for adolescents with eating disorders and consists of a brief series of sessions focused on returning the teenager to their expected developmental track and re-establishing typical, positive family relations.

Parental empowerment or parental self-efficacy (PSE) is a key concept in FBT and available research supports a view that improvements in PSE is one reason FBT is effective. Further, research suggests early change in PSE is a strong predictor of outcome. To help increase PSE, this book aims to help parents identify the things that can cause treatment to become stalled, as well as to help parents identify possible solutions that would allow them to move forward and effectively bring their child to recovery.

What Are Eating Disorders? (A Brief Overview)

It may be helpful for those parents new to EDs to learn a little more about each of the main types of EDs we discuss in this book.

Anorexia Nervosa (AN) is a psychiatric disorder characterized by restriction of caloric intake leading to low body weight, a fear of weight gain, and body image concerns. Lifetime prevalence of AN falls within the range of 0.1–3.6% for females, and 0–0.3% for males. The average onset of AN is generally thought to be around 13–19 years old. Of all psychiatric disorders, AN has the highest mortality rate of 10% per decade.

Bulimia Nervosa (BN) is characterized by recurrent episodes of binge eating and compensatory behaviors to prevent weight gain, such as self-induced vomiting, laxative misuse, fasting, and excessive exercise. Like AN, BN behaviors are driven by a desire to change one's shape and weight. BN typically onsets in adolescence. The lifetime prevalence estimates for BN range from 0.28% to 2.9%. BN has an approximate female-to-male ratio of 10:1 and a crude mortality rate of 2% per decade.

Binge Eating Disorder (BED) involves recurrent episodes of binge eating marked by distress, rapid eating, eating past the point of fullness, eating in the absence of hunger, eating alone due to embarrassment, and/or feeling disgusted afterward. BED typically onsets in late adolescence and early adulthood and beyond—a time when life aspirations such as jobs, career, and relationships are at the forefront. BED is estimated to affect 1.5% of women and 0.3% of men.

Avoidant/Restrictive Food Intake Disorder (ARFID) is characterized by highly selective, restrictive eating habits resulting in nutritional deficiencies. ARFID differs for AN or BN because there are not excessive concerns about body shape or weight. ARFID is marked by an early age of onset (from age 2 onwards) and an estimated prevalence rate of 7.2–17.4%. Nutritional deficiencies can lead to psychosocial impairment and medical problems, such as severe malnutrition, growth stunting, and dependence on enteral feeding. ARFID sometimes co-occurs with other neurodevelopmental diagnoses, such as autism spectrum disorder, attention-deficit hyperactivity disorder, and/or generalized anxiety disorder.

Overview of Content and Structure of the Book

Chapter 1: The First Challenge: Taking immediate and decisive action

This chapter helps parents appreciate the need to act quickly and decisively to help their child with an eating disorder. It describes some of the things that can get in the way of parents acting quickly and provides tips on how parents can identify if there is an obstacle that is preventing them from taking immediate effective action to counter the ED behaviors. Brief case vignettes are used to illustrate the importance of acting quickly. Throughout the chapter, parents are encouraged to act now and effectively to nourish their child back to health (if the young person needs to regain lost weight) and/or to intervene effectively to prevent their child from engaging in harmful ED behaviors.

Chapter 2: The Madness of Causes: Losing focus by trying to figure out why the eating disorder developed

This chapter focuses on the tendency of parents to spend time in the early stages of treatment trying to understand what the "root cause" of the ED was, in a belief that such an understanding will lead to a solution. Preoccupation with understanding causes tends to result in parents not taking effective action, as they frequently blame themselves, or each other, or someone else for "causing" the ED, and this anger or guilt gets in the way of parents' ability to take effective action to help their child. The chapter explains why looking for the cause of the ED is a strategy that usually does not lead to behavior change, even if a potential "cause" could be found. Case vignettes illustrate the concept that seeking causes wastes valuable time when what is needed instead is for parents to invest their energy in re-nourishing their child and/or preventing their child from engaging in harmful ED behaviors. Parents are encouraged to leave these etiological concerns aside for now and instead focus on finding a practical solution to the problem of the ED behaviors.

Chapter 3: Working Together: When we are in a lifeboat, we all need to row together

This chapter is about the vital importance of parents, and indeed the entire family, working together effectively to combat EDs. Brief case vignettes are used to describe how parents often struggle to reach agreement on a strategy to manage the ED, and also to illustrate how effective it can be when parents do work together. Parents are given tips on how to recognize signs that they may not be not in agreement, resulting in not taking a unified approach. Illustration of ways parents might turn this around and begin to work together more effectively are included. This chapter also addresses the challenges of divorced or separated parents caring for a child with an ED, and case vignettes illustrate how these parents can overcome conflicts to work together effectively to support their child to overcome the ED. This chapter also highlights the importance of harnessing the power of the *entire* family, including siblings in most instances, to overcome the ED. It addresses parental concerns that involving siblings in treatment may upset or harm them and also discusses situations where more than one child has an ED, or where parents worry that a sibling may develop an ED due to exposure to the first child's ED behaviors. In addition, the challenge some parents have of clinicians not always working well together is discussed. When clinicians don't work together, that can sometimes lead to parents getting mixed messages and this is something that can cause parents to get stalled due to uncertainty about what is the best course of action. Ideas about how parents can effectively tackle this problem if it occurs during their child's treatment are presented.

Chapter 4: Big Feelings: How too much worry about a child's emotions can undermine success

This chapter is concerned with a common tendency for parents to avoid challenging the ED behaviors due to worry about upsetting their child. Often the young person with the ED has been surreptitiously engaging in ED behaviors for some time prior to beginning FBT, and when parents then begin to intervene to change the ED behaviors, the child suddenly becomes very frightened and upset, a situation that can lead parents to feel that FBT "is making everything worse" rather than better. The chapter explains why the increase in the child's distress is usually a sign parents are making progress against the ED. The parents are encouraged to continue to pursue their efforts to intervene against the ED behaviors while also comforting their child. Case vignettes illustrate how parents sometimes struggle to take effective action to help their child because the "help" (prevention of restriction, purging and over-exercise) causes the child to become extremely distressed. Often the child's distress escalates to behavioral outbursts that are often quite out of usual character for the child. Parents are given tips on how to manage their child's emotions and the challenging ED behavioral outbursts. They are also given suggestions on how to manage their own emotions about upsetting their child, as well as tolerating conflict and difficult feelings being expressed in their family.

Chapter 5: Stop Blaming Your Child or Yourself: You're fighting an eating disorder, not your child or yourself

Many parents experience difficulty separating the eating disorder from the child. It describes a common error parents make where they see their child as willful or difficult rather than understanding that their child's challenging behaviors are manifestations of a serious psychological and medical illness. This chapter helps parents recognize if and when they are having difficulty externalizing the ED illness and blaming their child. Case vignettes illustrate how parents can move from being frustrated with their child to a situation where parents have increased empathy with the child's emotional state while at the same time understanding the need to take effective action to help their child battle the ED. Case vignettes also illustrate occasions when parents struggle to separate the ED from their child and make the mistake of 'listening' too much to their child, when in fact they are listening to the ED attempting to convince them that they should not intervene to make changes.

Chapter 6: Do Not Try to Reason With an Eating Disorder: Why trying to reason with a child with eating-disordered thinking doesn't work

This chapter addresses the parents' hope that reasoning with their child will be effective in resolving the eating disorder. They hope they can reason with their child and that the child will behave rationally once parents or treatment providers point out the dangers of the ED behaviors. The chapter describes how parents often get sidetracked by getting involved in "arguments with the ED" which become increasingly irrational and only waste parents' time and deplete them of the energy they need to challenge dangerous ED behaviors. Case vignettes illustrate situations where parents first struggled to understand that the ED was irrational, but then were able to move beyond frustrating arguments to a position of empathy and non-negotiable boundaries that allowed their efforts to intervene successfully against the ED.

Chapter 7: Deferring to Experts Is Not the Answer: How expecting other professionals to solve the problem can interfere with progress in FBT

Some parents have the belief that they should wait for the young person to develop motivation to change or to "buy into" the FBT treatment approach. Relatedly, some parents think that their child needs individual therapy for their eating disorder, usually due to a belief that individual therapy will lead to the young person gaining insight into the ED and that this insight will lead to a dissipation of the ED in the child's mind. The chapter stresses the importance of parents understanding that insight is often very limited in EDs and even when insight is present, it is not generally consistent enough to lead to behavior change. The chapter also highlights the need for parents to focus on providing their child with a level of support the child may not have ever previously needed. The chapter describes the importance of focusing on behavior change first because this is the most successful strategy to achieve physical and psychological recovery. Several case examples are used to illustrate situations where parents are stuck in treatment because their child had always been very reasonable and managed life well and so they expected them to be able to manage the ED too, especially when the young person sometimes appeared to have insight into how destructive the disorder was. However, once parents realized their child was not able to cope with the psychological challenge of the ED, they understood they needed to step in to take charge to help their child recover. The chapter also describes the worry that some parents have that FBT treatment does not take on all the problems their child has and should focus on additional challenges their child faces, such as depression, anxiety or OCD, or that the child should be in co-occurring individual therapy for such problems. The chapter explains why it is usually essential to focus on the eating disorder as the first goal of therapy, but also explains why it is necessary to prioritize ED recovery to make progress with other psychological symptoms and co-morbidities like depression, anxiety, and other behavioral problems.

Chapter 8: Why Is This So Hard?: How patience and persistence are the keys to success in FBT

A common pitfall for parents is to step back before the job is done. It describes why, for cases where a young person is underweight, it is important for parents to focus on providing their child with calorically dense foods even when these are more challenging for their child. It also highlights the importance of being consistent around food intake in order to achieve weight progress. This chapter also discusses how some parents believe that they need a dietician or a meal plan to re-nourish their child. It explains why parents are best placed to make the decisions together around what to feed their child and when and how to use dieticians helpfully. For cases where cessation of ED behaviors rather than weight gain is the goal, this chapter describes how parents must consistently do enough to break the destructive ED behavior patterns rather than just occasionally preventing a behavior, which will likely lead only to arguments and not to an effective disruption of the pattern. Case vignettes illustrate situations such as when parents get stuck in treatment due to not giving their child enough food to restore weight—though the actual amount appeared to parents to be "healthy"—and how treatment moved forward more effectively when the parents pushed to increase intake so that it was enough to make the crucial difference for recovery. Other case vignettes illustrate how important it is for parents to be consistent and effective in developing eating routines and disrupting and preventing behaviors such as binge eating, purging, or over-exercise when these are present.

Chapter 9: Does Everything Have to Stop?: Balancing academic progress, athletics, or activities, and ED recovery

This chapter describes how it can be hard to prioritize working on the ED over prioritizing progress in school, sports, and social activities at the start of FBT. Case examples illustrate the importance of setting these other things aside for a period when trying to change ED behaviors. The chapter also includes a discussion on how parents might manage return to sports or activities that place value on low weight, such as ballet, gymnastics, wrestling, cycling, or cross-country running, which may be a maintaining factor for the ED, or a risk factor for relapse. Case vignettes are used to illustrate ways parents successfully managed these common situations.

Chapter 10: Don't Give Up Too Soon: Why it is important to accomplish the goals of FBT to reduce the likelihood of relapse

In some cases of EDs where there is substantial clinical progress but the young person remains vulnerable to relapse because of ongoing symptoms, it is tempting for parents to stop intervening. For example, in AN, it is not uncommon for a young person to experience an uptick in distress when nearing recovery, and parents, reacting to the distress and believing that their child is no longer in crisis, agree to stop pushing for progress. The chapter describes how and why this decision often leads to behavioral regression or relapse. A case example is used to illustrate why parents can get lulled into believing that it will be a "good enough" outcome if they stop at what appears to be a reasonable weight, but how this in fact leaves the AN to fester and will frequently lead to weight loss and increase in ED symptoms. Similarly, parents can become fatigued and can give up too soon on the process of preventing destructive ED behaviors in BN, BED and ARFID, or Atypical ED presentations. Case vignettes are used to illustrate the importance of parents *outlasting* the ED behaviors and continuing to work to help until their child has attained a greater level of recovery.

Chapter 11: Find Support: Why it is important for parents to seek support from professionals, families, friends, and organizations

This chapter discusses issues of shame and stigma that parents of children with EDs commonly experience, and how this can lead to a delay in seeking support. It discusses how parents can maximize their ability to successfully combat their child's ED when they seek support, and highlights the importance of parents recognizing and making allowances for the burden of care associated with an ED, especially in the early phase of treatment. Emphasis is placed on the fact that the road to recovery can be long and that for most families there are some setbacks along the way. Case vignettes illustrate situations where parents experienced significant levels of stress and found it difficult to focus their energies on the treatment process, but then after seeking support from friends and family they became more successful in achieving weight progress, leading to the entire family feeling more optimistic. Emphasis is placed on the need for parents to seek support and also to support each other (for families where two or more parents are involved in caring for the child). This chapter also describes how parents sometimes feel they are "failing FBT" if there is not weight gain or other evidence of behavioral progress each week, and then they sometimes avoid therapy sessions due to shame. The discussion emphasizes that FBT aims to *support* parents to successfully complete a very difficult task, and when things are not going well the therapist will join with the parents to identify practical solutions that makes sense to them. Case vignettes are used to illustrate such a situation.

Chapter 12: Bringing It all Together and Moving On

This chapter pulls together the themes that have been discussed in the book, emphasizes the vital importance of the role of parents and the entire family in helping their child recover, and offers parents hope that their child can make a good recovery with their help. It reviews and summarizes the key themes from each chapter and describes how they are inter-related strategies that help parents guide their children's recovery. A resources section for parents who want to learn more is provided at the end of the book.

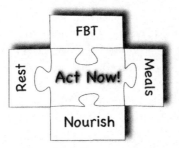

Figure 1.1 The first challenge: Taking immediate and decisive action
Nandini Datta

1
The First Challenge: Taking immediate and decisive action

Well begun is half done.
Aristotle

I wish I had realized sooner that the only way to make this work is to stop everything, everything, everything else, and attend to just this one vital thing, getting my child better.
Parent of young person with an eating disorder

Over years of working with families facing eating disorders, we clinicians often observed that those families who got off to a good start in FBT tended to continue to make steady progress and to have the best outcomes. This clinical observation was confirmed in an important research study that found that, amongst underweight young people with Anorexia Nervosa (AN), those who gained about 6 pounds (2.4 kg) in the first four weeks of FBT had about an 80% chance of going on to make a full recovery. Conversely, those who did *not* gain well in the first four weeks had about a 70% chance of *not* fully recovering. Similarly, for adolescents with Bulimia Nervosa (BN), studies suggest that reducing purging and binge eating frequency early in FBT (by sessions 4–6) predicts improved outcomes. These are some of the reasons why we strongly encourage all parents to take immediate and decisive action to help their child. We urge them to move swiftly, to put everything else

DOI: 10.4324/9781003353041-2

on hold, and to focus their energy on the effort to get their child solidly on the path to recovery. However, for many reasons, parents can struggle to get traction in those first weeks of treatment. For parents of young people with AN or BN often their child's eating disorder diagnosis comes as a tremendous shock. Often there can be a period of several weeks or even months where parents have difficulty processing the fact that their child has been stricken with a life-threatening and life-limiting illness. In some cases of Avoidant/ Restrictive Food Intake Disorder (ARFID), the challenge is that the child likely has always resisted eating and due to the long-term nature of the struggle parents often feel helpless or hopeless about their ability to feed their children. In all ED cases parents may have become accustomed to the way their child eats, through what is a common psychological process of accommodation to a challenging situation. These psychological responses of shock or habituation happen with other diagnoses also, but with other illnesses, even if parents are struggling to come to terms with what is happening, so long as they take the child to their medical appointments then there is often little adverse impact on the child's prognosis and treatment. Our challenge is that when we are using FBT to treat a young person with an eating disorder, the parents must take an active and central role in their child's recovery. In FBT, it is usually the actions of the family, and not the clinicians directly, that will bring about the child's recovery. And so, the parents' difficulty with grasping the seriousness of the situation, or with understanding the enormity of what must be done every day to help the young person, can unfortunately impede the young person's chances of recovery.

One of the other major impediments to quick progress against the eating disorder is a tendency of some parents to overestimate their child's ability to go along with the treatment plan. This makes sense when we consider how hard it is for parents to comprehend that their child with AN or BN will often desperately want to continue with the eating disorder behaviors *no matter what the risks or costs to them.* It can take parents some time to comprehend that their previously rational, reasonable, agreeable, child, who mostly used to do what they asked with minimal opposition (i.e., finish their homework, practice piano every day, brush their teeth every night) will now refuse outright when their parents make the most reasonable demand in the world: Eat enough food to ensure health and stop other behaviors that keep eating-disordered thinking in place. *Of course initially* parents expect their child will do as doctors say when the gravity of the situation is explained to them and *of course* it is quite shocking to parents when their child outright refuses to cooperate. It takes a long time to understand how irrational eating disorder behaviors and cognitions are and no parent could be expected to understand them in the beginning.

Parents often lose ground in the fight against the eating disorder because in the early stages they may fail to appreciate just how much effort it is going to take every day to get progress. When faced with their child's resistance to making changes, many parents will respond with repeated attempts to reason with their child in an effort to get them to "see sense" (see Chapter 6). Parents can waste precious time at this point, often spending weeks expecting that their child will come around to doing as they have been told. And because they believe this will happen, parents make the mistake of assuming their child can manage situations like eating independently at school, or eating unsupervised at home, or managing exercise levels appropriately (see Chapter 9).

FBT therapists understand that when it comes to many eating-disordered behaviors it is highly unlikely that the young person is going to be able to work with their parents in a cooperative way at the beginning, but that is because the therapist knows how eating disorders change a young person's thinking and behavior. Parents usually don't know that much about eating disorders, they only know their own child, and so they expect that their child will behave pretty much in their normal way. It can take parents a long time to adjust to the way the eating disorder impacts their child's thinking and behavior. All too often, it is only after many weeks of failure to make progress against the eating disorder that parents decide to step in and fully take charge of every eating situation and every situation where the young person could engage in purging or exercise; and while they can still have success at that point, there have been weeks and even months of time when the ED has been getting stronger while the young person and family have been feeling weaker and less effective.

To appreciate how this transpires the following vignettes are some examples of families who struggled in the beginning stages of their child's eating disorders.

A Slow Start in FBT for Anorexia Nervosa

Laurie and Steve, the parents of 15-year-old Piper, were shocked by their daughter's diagnosis of AN. Up until that moment in time, everything in their lives had been going well. Theirs was a big, busy household. They had three children, a dog, two cats and a rabbit. They had worked hard to build their careers and to raise their children together with love and with appropriate boundaries and discipline. Together they had navigated the many challenges of pregnancies and taking care of infants and managing toddlers' tantrums and helping children adjust to school and then to the changes of early the adolescent years. Mostly things had gone without serious trouble. Their children had always been happy in school, they played soccer, softball, basketball, and they each had a good group of friends. Piper was a wonderful artist and she also liked singing and dancing. The family liked to go for hikes on weekends. They were big sports fans and regularly went to games together. They took ski trips in the winter and they surfed in summer. They were an active, happy, outgoing family.

Laurie and Steve juggled their time between the demands of their jobs and the busy schedules of their three kids and their activities. Piper had started high school the previous fall, and she had signed up for the school's musical theater group. The oldest child, Zach, played softball, had training two nights per week, and he also had games on weekends, usually in different places to Piper's activities. The youngest child, Gregory, played soccer, with practice one night a week plus a game most weekends. Laurie and Steve used to joke that they needed a third parent to keep up with the logistical demands of driving three kids to three different places at the same time. Steve often had to travel with work, and Laurie had a complicated arrangement with carpools with other parents in order to get the kids to where they needed to be. It was all a bit "crazy busy" but everyone was happy.

After their first session of FBT, when the therapist explained the seriousness of the AN, and explained that they needed to take charge of the situation, Laurie and Steve talked about it, and they did make lots of changes. They explained to Piper that she must eat more. They put together a breakfast for her and placed it on the table for her to eat. They packed her a lunch for Piper to bring to school. They sat with her for dinner in the evening. They encouraged her to eat snacks.

At their second FBT session, Laurie and Steve were surprised to learn that Piper hadn't gained weight. They felt they were doing all they could. Their therapist asked about where and when meals happened, what was on the plate, and who was present. Laurie and Steve explained that they were all in a hurry to get out to work and school in the mornings, so they couldn't sit at the table with Piper for very long. They explained that she ate her lunch and snack at school, with her friends. She had promised them she was eating all the food, they explained. They had dinner together, but it was a stressful experience, as Piper argued that she had already had a lot of food earlier in the day, said she felt full, said she had a pain in her stomach from eating so much. She did not usually finish the entire portion at dinner.

The therapist repeated the suggestion that Laurie and Steve should focus on what level of their support might be necessary in order for Piper to make good weight progress. She explained that many parents found that they needed to take their child out of school in the initial weeks, or at least go to the school to supervise lunches and snacks to make sure their child was eating. She explained that at this point in recovery, a general rule is that "if you didn't see the food being eaten, it didn't happen."

Laurie and Steve couldn't imagine how they would manage to supervise meals during the day. Neither one of them could stop working, they said. And what's more, Piper really wanted to stay in school. She was upset at the idea of missing classes, as she would feel she was getting behind on her schoolwork.

Piper gained a pound the next week. Then the next week she lost a pound. At the fourth FBT session, her net weight gain from session one was only one pound. What's more, Piper was more upset than ever. She was angry her parents were trying to "force" her to eat more, she was angry about coming for treatment. She was distraught about gaining that one pound.

Meanwhile, her parents were feeling fatigued and demoralized. And they were very, very worried about their child not getting better. By week four they said they thought "FBT is not working" and wondered if Piper needed a different kind of treatment.

The therapist observed that it seemed they expected life should go on pretty much as normal while they figured out how to re-nourish Piper. She helped them reflect on why they expected this should be possible. On the surface of it, it was a reasonable assumption. If Piper had not had AN, and had lost weight for some other reason, it might be possible for her to restore weight without much change needed in their lives. Steve and Laurie were failing to grasp the enormity of the challenge before them.

Their therapist reminded them of the seriousness of the AN and she told them directly that Piper was not recovering. She asked them to think about what else they could do, about how far they would go to ensure their child   did make progress. In talking it over together, Steve and Laurie realized that they needed to take "drastic action" rather than continue to expect things would just get better.

The parents decided that for the next week they would take Piper out of school and all her activities. Laurie took time off work and stayed home for the entire week. Steve cancelled a scheduled business trip and worked from home so that he could also be present for mealtimes. They explained to some of their friends that Piper was ill and they asked for their help with carpools for the boys' sports activities. They were determined that they would make significant, measurable progress in that week.

And they did. At the next session, Piper was up a full 2 pounds. This gave a much-needed boost to Steve and Laurie's confidence. They decided they could keep doing the same things for another week. And then the next week she was up another 1.8 pounds. Steve and Laurie both commented that although they had thought it would be very hard, or even impossible, to stop everything and just focus on re-nourishing Piper, actually they found it was easier to do this than to do what they had first tried, which was to pretty much keep on as normal. When they stopped everything, it is true that they had to put in even more effort, but the results they got helped them feel hopeful and confident rather than frightened and helpless.

The family moved through phases 1, 2, and 3 of treatment as Piper went from strength to strength. After about a year of treatment Piper made a full recovery both physically and psychologically.

Steve said,

> I wish we hadn't wasted time trying to carry on as normal. We didn't understand how much help Piper actually needed. It was devastating not to make the weight progress every week. We felt we were trying so hard and not getting results, so we felt more and more anxious. Once we stopped doing everything else and just concentrated on fighting the ED, then we began to make real progress each week. Those successful weight checks reassured us we were doing the right thing. Once we knew we were on the right road, then we knew we could keep going. Even if it was an uphill road, it was the right road, it would get us to where we needed to go.

Laurie said,

> This is like when your baby is first born. You can't expect life to go on like normal. With a newborn, all of your time, day and night, is going to go into feeding and caring for your child. Now

Piper has this illness, I see that I need to do the same thing, spend my days and nights with her, caring for her, feeding her. And I shouldn't expect to do anything else. And I need my husband and my family and friends to pitch in to help me, just like when she was an infant.

Hesitant Start in Treating an Adolescent with Bulimia Nervosa

Here is a description of a family of a young person with Bulimia Nervosa who also struggled to get going in the first stage of treatment.

Marisol had been having emotional difficulties for a couple of years before her parents, David and Angelica, became worried about her eating. When she was in eighth grade, her best friend moved away, and Marisol struggled to find her niche with the other girls. Then, when she started high school the next year, she seemed to find the transition difficult. It was towards the end of that first year of high school that David and Angelica noticed that Marisol seemed to be eating in an erratic way, at times refusing to eat for hours on end, and then at times eating a lot all at once. They didn't know she was also making herself vomit until after they first brought her to a doctor. The doctor explained that Marisol had an eating disorder and she referred them to an FBT therapist.

During their first sessions of FBT, the therapist explained that for people with BN, restriction will usually trigger a binge eating episode, which will in turn lead to purging. Following this cycle, the young person usually feels terribly anxious about losing control and overeating, which leads them to want to restrict, and so the cycle will start again.

The therapist explained that David and Angelica should ensure Marisol ate at regular intervals and at the same time should stop Marisol from engaging in binge episodes as much as possible. And she also urged them to prevent Marisol from purging by setting some rules in place around use of bathroom after meals. And in addition, the therapist encouraged them to include feared foods in Marisol's meals, so that she could learn how to manage these trigger foods without engaging in binge eating and purge episodes.

Marisol was desperately upset by what the therapist suggested. She felt out of control during binge eating episodes, when she ate large amounts of food without being able to stop herself. She experienced an urgent need to vomit afterwards, in order to attain both physical and psychological relief. Marisol did very much want the binge eating to stop, but she absolutely did not want to stop restricting or purging. She was already so upset about the amount of food she consumed during binge eating episodes and she was terrified she would gain a lot of weight if she increased her food intake by eating regularly.

David and Angelica tried to set in place a system of regular eating for Marisol. But she resisted their efforts. She said she felt nauseous in the mornings. She said she would eat a snack at the first break time in school. Her parents packed her lunch each day and Marisol told them she always ate it all. At dinnertime, she would only eat a small portion and she refused to eat fried foods or carbs including rice, potatoes, or pasta. David and Angelica felt consoled by the fact that "she is eating most of it" and thought that maybe it wasn't very serious that she refused the carbs. After all, they reasoned, a lot of people don't eat carbs and are perfectly healthy.

On the weekends, Marisol slept late, so that by the time she was out of bed it was lunchtime rather than breakfast time. She stayed up late into the night and the next day the parents would notice there was a lot of food missing. Marisol spent a lot of time alone in her room, but then, parents felt, this is normal for teenagers. They felt uncomfortable "invading her privacy" by observing her in the bathroom and didn't ask Marisol if she was vomiting, mostly because Marisol was so uncomfortable talking about it.

For the first six weeks of FBT therapy, Marisol's parents struggled to see where they needed to intervene to help her. Her weight was in the normal to low-normal range, so they did not have a clear weight-gain target. David and Angelica attempted to balance trying to make sure Marisol was eating with not wanting to "push" her or upset her too much. Despite their efforts to avoid upsetting her, Marisol's mood was low, irritable, and oversensitive. Talking about it seemed to just upset her. She seemed more and more unhappy.

Their therapist asked the parents to identify what they thought the eating disorder behaviors were and to identify what they thought needed to change for Marisol to be healthy and happy. This helped David and

Angelica reflect that they had been accepting that Marisol's eating was "good enough" rather than assertively working to make changes to Marisol's destructive eating pattern. The therapist emphasized that the pattern of restriction, binge eating and purging involves extremely serious medical risks and also has a very significant negative impact on a person's mood, on their ability to regulate their emotions, and on their self-esteem. She asked David and Angelica whether, after six weeks of therapy, they were confident that Marisol was now on the road to recovery. David and Angelica both immediately said no, in a moment that surprised them in its clarity. The therapist asked them to talk together and to consider whether what they were doing was enough to make the crucial difference to help Marisol recover. They both felt that more change was needed and they realized that Marisol needed them to take charge more assertively and bring about change.

David and Angelica decided to step in more assertively to ensure that Marisol ate regularly. They decided she needed to eat breakfast every day before going to school. They began to wake her up on weekends to make sure she started to eat earlier in the day. They stayed up with her until she went to bed at night, so that she was less likely to engage in secretive binge eating. They implemented a rule where there were no bathroom visits for at least an hour after eating. Instead of letting her spend all her time alone in her room, they asked her to spend more time with them, doing activities she enjoyed. Because they noticed that Marisol was inclined to binge eat in the evenings after meals, they began to put activities into the time period.

As they began to intervene more assertively, it became apparent to David and Angelica that Marisol had been purging much more frequently than they had realized. When they prevented her from being in the bathroom, her frequent agitation made it clear that she had been purging several times per day, though David and Angelica had thought it was happening no more than once or twice per week. When they insisted that she eat normal portions of food at regular intervals, Marisol's level of distress was such that it was apparent that her eating disorder thoughts and feelings were much stronger than they had realized.

Their therapist encouraged David and Angelica to push through the difficult period, and over the next couple of months Marisol's eating pattern improved significantly. What's more, her mood improved week by week. She became more cheerful, more confident, more resilient in the face of setbacks.

Struggling Getting Started in FBT in a Child with ARFID

Many parents of children with ARFID typically say they have been struggling to feed their children from the day they were born. Some children with ARFID have never eaten normally and some either have very little interest in eating or are extremely "picky eaters" who will eat only a few different foods. They are the children who will freeze at the sight of new foods on their plate, spit out foods with expressions of exaggerated disgust, and suddenly vehemently reject a food that they had eaten every day for years. Their parents have usually been on the receiving end of lots of well-intended advice that might have been helpful if their children didn't have ARFID, e.g., "don't give in to his demands for a particular food. Present him with the food you want him to eat and refuse to give him his preferred food until he's eaten the other food first," and "sit at the table together and make mealtimes fun." And then there's the oft-repeated (but in the case of ARFID kids, utterly untrue) "he'll eat if he's hungry enough." All of this may be good feeding advice for most children, but it won't help at all with a child with ARFID, who generally will not respond normally to hunger cues, will not eat nearly enough if left to his own devices, and who, on being presented with a small portion of a new food, may dissolve into such an anxious tantrum that he will reject the entire meal, not just the scary new food.

Because it can take a long time for a child to be diagnosed with ARFID, most of these parents have been through experiences where they felt they were utterly failing at that most basic of parental responsibilities, nourishing their child. And they've usually had experiences where they've felt judged by doctors and by friends and family members as they've struggled to get their child to eat. And because the struggle has usually been going on for years, it's not surprising that most parents who start with FBT for ARFID take a bit of time to get going with making changes.

Here's an example of an ARFID family that struggled to get off the ground with FBT:

From the day he was born, Henry had been hard to feed. He cried all the time. He vomited constantly. The doctors diagnosed him with reflux and prescribed medication, which helped, but he still didn't seem much interested in eating. When his parents, Carla and Jeff, introduced solid foods, Henry mostly spat them out in disgust. They kept Henry on formula until he was over 3 years old because he so adamantly refused most other foods. When they took him to the doctor for his checkups, Henry didn't make his expected weight gains, especially as he moved beyond the toddler years. By the time they started FBT for ARFID, when Henry was 6 years old, he was in the bottom 1% of boys his age for weight and the bottom 3% for height. He ate very small portions, he ate a very limited range of foods, and he became anxious if a new food was even suggested.

Both Carla and Jeff felt anxious about Henry's eating, and at the same time, the problem had been going on so long that they had become used to it. "He's always been small," they said, "but we're worried about how picky he is. We want to get him to eat a wider variety of foods."

Although Carla and Jeff were concerned mostly about Henry's narrow range of foods, the FBT therapist was more concerned about his low weight and slow growth progress. "Maybe he's always been small because he's never been eating enough," she suggested. "That's one of the main risks with kids with ARFID, growth stunting. And Henry is very small for his age, and very, very low weight."

The therapist worked to identify what would be their main goals for treatment, especially in the early stages. Carla and Jeff both felt that their main goal was to successfully introduce new foods to increase Henry's range. They made a list of his accepted foods, which included Goldfish crackers, Cheerios (dry), chicken nuggets, garlic bread, small pasta shapes with butter, cookies, ice cream, cake, candy. Carla and Jeff wanted Henry to begin to eat fruit, vegetables, and more proteins like meat or eggs.

Carla and Jeff also wanted Henry to get better at sitting at the table during mealtimes. Henry was a very active child, and in fact he was waiting to be assessed for ADHD. In sessions, which were held over a videoconferencing platform, Henry ran around the room, jumped up and down on the couch, chattered to his parents even if they were mid-conversation, and generally was full of activity. Henry had two younger siblings, aged 3 years and 14 months, who were usually in the room for the sessions also. There was a lot of distraction in this busy household with three young children, and Henry was probably the most active of everyone. For the family meal session, while his siblings sat eating in their highchairs, Henry sat down only for a few minutes. He talked non-stop, and showed little interest in his food. He soon was up and about roaming around the living area, with his parents having to call him over every time they wanted him to take a bite of his food.

Carla really wanted Henry to eat some fruit. She explained that Henry's overall diet consisted of almost entirely "white" foods, and she worried he was not getting the full range of nutrients he needed. She and Jeff decided that they would work on getting Henry to eat a piece of apple every day. They both said they knew that Henry needed to increase his weight, and they reasoned that if they increased the number of different foods he would eat that this would naturally lead to an increase in the amount eaten too.

Over the next several weeks, Carla and Jeff worked to get Henry to eat a piece of apple every day. Henry would take the piece of apple, sniff it, then put it back down. At first, it took a lot of persuasion to get him to eat one bite. Sometimes he would eat one whole piece (one sixth of the full apple). Sometimes he even ate two pieces of apple. After a few weeks, with no significant or lasting progress, Carla and Jeff were frustrated and they were beginning to find it harder to keep up the routine of presenting the new foods regularly.

Each week, they would check Henry's weight, but there was no change. Henry was not gaining anything despite all their efforts. The FBT therapist worked to help Carla and Jeff see that at this point the main problem was that Henry was extremely low weight and was not growing well, and the best thing they could do to help him first was to increase the *amount* of food he was eating. It took Carla and Jeff some time to come to realize that they were putting a lot of effort into trying to change something—increasing the range of foods he would eat—that wasn't going to be the thing that would really make a difference in Henry's health at this point. Henry needed to eat a lot more food, and even if they got him to eat a whole apple every day this wasn't going to make much difference to his weight and growth progress. They realized that they needed to figure out how to get him to eat more every day, even if it meant just eating more of the foods he already accepted.

Part of the reason it took Carla and Jeff some time to grasp the idea that the main problem was that Henry was not eating enough was that much of the focus of *other peoples'* comments and concerns over the years had been around Henry's extreme picky eating rather than his low weight. They had felt they were "bad parents" because their child ate such a limited range of foods. They worried that he was not getting enough nutrients because he was not eating fruit and vegetables, but they had been less focused on the fact that he was significantly malnourished not so much because he was not eating a wide range of foods but because he was simply not eating enough of any food to be healthy.

Once Carla and Jeff saw they were not making progress because they were putting a lot of energy into a task that was not likely to bring the result they needed, they were able to pivot and put their energy into working out how to increase the amount of food Henry ate. "We need to give him more of the stuff he does eat," Jeff said. "Whenever, wherever he wants it." They began to give Henry an afternoon snack in the car on the way home from school, because they realized that Henry ate a little better when he was distracted on car journeys. They asked the school to arrange to have Henry taken out of class 15 minutes before lunch so he could eat just outside the school's administrative office, and then he would join his friends at lunchtime to have social time. At home, they decided to give Henry more garlic bread and chicken nuggets, as these were foods with high caloric density that he ate without resistance. They figured that even if it's not optimal nutrition, Henry's body would still use the energy to grow. They aimed for a "good enough" diet with the emphasis being on weight gain.

Henry did then begin to make weight progress. And once this was happening, Carla and Jeff felt reassured and more confident. This actually helped them to keep up with their plan of introducing apples to Henry's food list. This had been a good idea, it was just that they needed to figure out where to put their focus first. The family finished up FBT, but Carla and Jeff kept going with their strategies to ensure Henry had sufficient nutrition. They understood that the nature of ARFID is that it is a long-term condition and that Henry would need support with nutrition for a long time. Carla and Jeff felt that the skills they learned in FBT helped them understand how to work together going forward so that they could keep Henry healthy and happy and also ensure that they felt happier about how they were managing the challenges that Henry's ARFID presented to them all as a family.

In each of these cases, families struggled to get momentum in their efforts to combat their child's eating disorder. As each family began to overcome the elements that were impeding them, they not only made progress against the eating disorder, but, importantly, they also began to feel confident in their efforts. Once these parents began to see they were making progress in helping their child recover from their eating disorder, it became a little easier for them to keep going. It is very difficult to persist in doing something that is enormously difficult unless you can see that you are getting somewhere for all of your efforts. The sense of hope and mastery the parents experienced by making early progress were vitally important elements that support these families in their journey to recovery.

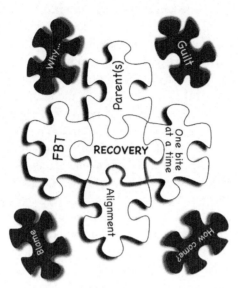

Figure 2.1 The madness of causes: Losing focus by trying to figure out why the eating disorder developed
Nandini Datta

2

The Madness of Causes: Losing focus by trying to figure out why the eating disorder developed

> I just want to know why this happened.... If we knew why, I think
> I would feel so much better and know how to be helpful.
>> Parent at the beginning of FBT

Parents want to help their children get over their eating disorder. Many parents sometimes think it is necessary to know *why* their child developed an eating disorder if they are going to be helpful. This is completely understandable, but it turns out that a focus on causes can get in the way of actually helping your child with their eating disorder.

DOI: 10.4324/9781003353041-3

It is important to appreciate that parents might want to focus on the cause of the eating disorder. For one thing, it is human nature to try to make sense of things. The world is full of unexpected, random, and chaotic events that beg for explanation even if many occur completely by chance. Humans create myths, stories, and follow superstitions that help us manage our worries about things that are beyond our control. For many things that happen there are no real reasons that explain them. That said, in medicine we often understand at least some of the reasons why certain illnesses and diseases occur. We know that smoking and exposure to asbestos can cause lung cancer. We know that genetic factors can cause disorders like Huntington's and sickle cell anemia. We know that certain bacterial and viral infections cause pneumonia. We know overexposure to the sun can cause skin cancer. However, for most of these, even understanding some of the reasons why a disease develops seldom fully explains why the disease develops in a specific person at a specific time. Some people with the exact same exposure (or risk factor) do not develop the disease while others do. Still, by seeking to understand why a disease develops we hope to identify ways to prevent the development of the disease (i.e., stopping smoking, using sunscreen) and to develop treatments that address causes (i.e., medications or treatment protocols matched specifically to genetic markers for types of breast cancer). However, even in medicine we treat the symptoms more often than the cause. We use surgery to remove a cancerous lesion, we use insulin to treat diabetes, beta blockers to manage cardiac arrhythmias—none of these actually treat the reason why the disease developed, but they do treat the disease and in some cases cure it (e.g., skin cancer, chemotherapy for breast cancer).

In psychology, psychiatry, and behavioral health generally, we need to be more realistic about our expectation about understanding why someone develops a mental health disorder. Our understanding of the underlying mechanisms of how these disorders develop—while advancing—is still in its infancy in many ways. We talk about the brain basis of mental disorders, but we know that hormones, inflammation, toxins, environment stress, genetics, and many other factors contribute to the risk for mental illness. Sometimes clinicians and scientists use the phrase "multi-factorial" to describe the many possible elements of causation. In mental disorders "multi-factorial" means that there are several factors that come together that have cause or lead to the development of the disorder. In fact, while accurate, this phrase is actually not particularly helpful in a specific case and provides little reassurance about what might be the real contributors of the disorder developing. We understand that there are genetic vulnerabilities for mental disorders; we know that environmental stressors like abuse and trauma increase risk for mental disorders generally; and we know that social determinants such as lack of access to emotional and developmental support also contribute to the risk for mental disorders. Still, none of these explains why a particular child develops a specific mental disorder. Luckily—as in the rest of medicine— many effective treatments used in mental health disorders do not try to address the cause of the disorder, but instead focus on changing and/or eliminating the symptoms.

Eating disorders are no different from other mental and behavioral disorders in the sense that our understanding of the cause of these disorders is fraught with uncertainty. There are genetic risk factors and some eating disorders appear to run in families, though environmental factors play a part as well. We know that there are developmental factors that also potentially play a role for some eating disorders as they onset typically in the context of puberty (e.g., Anorexia Nervosa). Psychosocial factors are also important as the media continue to present idealized body images that glamorize and fetishize specific body types that contribute to the risk for developing eating disorders, perhaps especially Bulimia Nervosa. Trauma is often found in the histories of young persons with eating disorders, but these traumas are not usually specific risk factors, meaning they do not explain why the young person developed an eating disorder rather than depression or anxiety disorders that are also common outcomes of a trauma history. So, while it is dissatisfying in many ways to admit that we do not know the underlying cause of eating disorders, it is in fact important to acknowledge this and not shy away from the truth of it and the implications this has for treatment.

What does it mean for treatment of eating disorders if we do not focus treatment on what the cause of the disorder is? It can mean many things—as parents it may be profoundly disappointing to accept therapy will not focus on identifying a cause. The wish to have an explanation as to why this has happened to your child is very compelling and hard for many parents to surrender. It can also lead to questioning the validity of the therapy—after all, many parents are told by therapists, and this is reinforced in the popular press and media, that it is a key tenet of psychotherapy to identify and address the underlying cause of the disorder if treatment is to be truly successful. This perspective is a holdover from the psychoanalytic tradition that posited that resolving internal unconscious conflict requires understanding the cause. However, this tenet does not apply to many other forms of psychosocial interventions including cognitive behavioral therapy, interpersonal therapy, and family systems therapy where the focus of the therapy is not on causation but instead on factors that maintain the disturbed behavior or cognitions.

These factors may be specific behaviors, distorted cognitions, emotional instability, ways of communicating, or other factors. The point is that like medical treatments that address and treat symptoms rather than causes, these approaches are effective without a focus on why the disorder developed, but instead on how it is maintained. FBT is also a therapy that does not aim to identify or address *why* a young person developed an eating disorder. Instead it aims to help families—and especially parents—identify ways to help their child overcome their eating disorder by addressing maintaining factors.

In each of the case illustrations that follow, parents have to overcome their initial impulse to focus on why the eating disorder developed in their child instead of facing the eating-disordered behaviors to start with.

How Focusing on the Cause of Anorexia Nervosa Interferes With Progress in FBT for AN

Bea was 13 when she began restricting her eating. She was the only child of two professional parents who doted on her. She had been a strong-willed child but also self-motivated from an early age. She was an excellent student and played soccer with a local league. When she went in for a routine physical required by her soccer team, her parents were shocked when they were told that Bea was now severely under-weight and nearing needing to be hospitalized because her heart rate was very slow. Both parents started reading anything they could find on AN, but nothing seemed to answer their most burning questions: How did this happen to their daughter? What had they done wrong to cause this? They were desperate to understand why Bea had gotten so ill, so it was not surprising that when they arrived for their first session of FBT they wanted to ask the therapist these crucial questions. When the therapist explained to them that there was no clear scientific evidence that had yet identified why a person developed AN, both parents were reluctant to accept this. They left the session frustrated and confused and were uncertain about whether to continue treatment. During the week between the first and second sessions, Bea's parent explored other options—individual therapy, residential treatment, day programs—but couldn't decide amongst them, so they reluctantly attended the second FBT session, which included eating a meal with the therapist there to coach them about how to be more effective in re-nourishing their daughter. They packed Bea's now "usual" lunch of plain rice cakes, carrots and celery sticks, and fat-free milk for the session. Bea ate the lunch they brought, but when the therapist asked her parents if they thought she would gain weight as a result, they admitted that they knew it was not enough, but they did not want to force her to eat as they were uncertain why she wasn't eating—Did she have an undetected medical problem? Did she have an emotional trauma that she needed help with? Was she having trouble with friends? Was she angry at them for the fact that they both worked and perhaps had not given her the attention she wanted or needed? The therapist tried to help the family focus their efforts on helping Bea eat but they were frozen in their tracks by these worries about why AN developed and afraid of making it worse if they did not figure it out.

The worries and concerns of Bea's parents are common ones at the beginning of FBT for AN, but if they persist, they can derail the therapy and make the chances of recovery diminish considerably. Bea's parents were deeply caring and wanted to do the right thing, the best thing, the thing that would cure Bea, but their focus on trying to figure out the cause was delaying them from taking any action to help Bea. Their fear of doing the wrong thing is understandable, but it was also forestalling them almost completely in taking action. In this instance their wish for the "perfect" answer is actually truly the enemy of the "good." Studies support that parents who early on take a hands-on practical approach to helping their child with AN change undereating and other related behaviors, rather than waiting to do anything until they understand "why" the disorder developed, help their children gain weight faster and increase their chances of recovery by a large margin as well as reduce the risk for medical hospitalization due to severe malnutrition.

Bea's parents again struggled about whether to continue FBT but came to the third session where they learned that Bea's weight had dropped again. The therapist asked if they expected this and both of them reluctantly admitted that they were not surprised because Bea was not eating any more on her own and they had not tried to help her directly. The therapist kindly and supportively pointed out that she understood their hesitancy, but asked them to consider what they wanted to do because if they continued on their current path, there was little doubt that Bea would end up in the hospital at least for a time, but ultimately they would face these dilemmas at home again as soon as she was discharged. Bea was herself mostly silent during the sessions, keeping a stoic posture, but when the therapist suggested again that the parents try something different, even for a short while, and take charge of Bea's meals and stop her exercising, she flew into a rage, yelling profanities at the therapist first, then begging her parents to not listen to the therapist. She claimed she was fine and was doing better despite the continued downward trend of her already low weight. Her parents sat wide-eyed and astonished at Bea's behavior. The therapist asked them to consider just how different Bea's behavior was now compared to before she had gotten ill. While this did nothing to calm Bea down, the parents were more receptive to seeing the need for doing something to change things as they saw Bea getting more sick, not better at all. At the end of the session, the therapist asked the parents to decide together if they were willing to take charge of Bea's eating and how they might get started.

Bea's behavior and the therapist's continued supportive non-critical insistence that the parents consider other options helped them to start to move out of the "deer in the headlights" position that their focus on why Bea had developed AN and the need to address that had held them in place for several weeks. During the weeks that followed, Bea's parents began to structure mealtimes, chose foods for her to eat that would help her gain weight, insist that she eat before going to school, and prohibit her from running. Bea was not very cooperative with any of these changes initially and tried hard to make her parents feel bad about their insistence, but because they saw weight gain and the threat of hospitalization diminishing, they kept at it despite Bea's protests. The therapist helped them keep focused on how they were helping, not the cause of AN, by identifying progress Bea was making without them discussing why she developed AN.

Parents of children who develop AN struggle with wanting to know why this happened in part because for most of them, the development of AN comes out of the blue and seems to have few if any real harbingers of trouble. While the onset of AN can be insidious, frank symptoms manifest fairly quickly— usually between three and six months—so the problem is both sudden and unexpected, making the wish to identify a clear cause compelling for many. Children who develop AN are of course as different from one another as are the families they come from, but one thing common to most is that the child has been seen as generally functioning well or very well in most cases so trouble is also unexpected for this reason. Some parents cling to a hope that a medical explanation will be found—an infection, a hormone problem, or a gastrointestinal problem—to explain the symptoms of AN. The hope here may be that a medical problem can be more easily treated effectively than a mental health problem, or it may be that a physical health problem is more acceptable to some parents than an emotional or behavioral problem for which they might feel responsible or blamed. Of course in some cases these hopes and fears may be well founded, but for the vast majority of cases of AN, they are not and the focus on causation becomes an obstacle that adds to the burden of trying to help change the maintaining behaviors that keep AN in place.

> Bea's parents, even with their reservations, pressed for change in her eating and insisted that she would only be able to do the things she wanted when she was nutritionally sound to do them. This was not a punitive stance, but one that would not "give in" to the irrational fears and anxieties that AN instilled in Bea. By the time they reached the latter part of treatment, both parents had largely let go of their quest to find the cause of AN and instead embraced the improvements they had helped her to make.

How Focusing on the Cause of Bulimia Nervosa and Binge Eating Interferes with FBT for BN

> Lila was 16 when her parents heard her throwing up in the bathroom toilet. She claimed it had happened just that once and that she was feeling sick. They wanted to believe Lila so they gave her the benefit of the doubt as they had on a number of other occasions about other problematic behaviors like staying out late, bad grades, and emotional outbursts. They were not overly strict parents and they appreciated that being a teenager was difficult. However, when they caught her purging again a week later, they knew they had to intervene so they made an appointment with Lila's pediatrician. They had also noticed large amounts of food going missing from cabinets and found large quantities of candy wrappers and empty cereal boxes in the trash. The pediatrician was concerned about Lila and wanted to rule out a physical origin for her behavior so ordered a range of medical tests including laboratory blood chemistries, a lung X-ray, and even an upper GI study. None of these tests found anything definitive, but Lila still claimed

that she had problems with her stomach that explained her behavior. Her parents were uncertain what to do, but the pediatrician suggested a mental health clinician meet with Lila for a diagnostic assessment and treatment recommendations. The parents made the appointment and Lila met with the clinician who developed sufficient rapport with Lila to allow her to admit to the voluntary nature of her binge eating, purging, her anxieties about weight and appearance, and her failed attempts at dieting. A diagnosis of Bulimia Nervosa (BN) was made and the parents chose FBT as the treatment they would use. However, there were problems from the start as Lila did not want her parents involved. She said they were treating her like a child and she could help herself. Lila's parents wanted to help her, but thought that her problems were rooted in something that they didn't understand and that they believed likely explained a lot of her other problems with friends and emotions.

Like many parents with a teenager who develops BN or Binge Eating Disorder (BED), Lila's parents were confused about how to help, and this also meant for them a reasonable desire that the treatment focus on what was causing all of Lila's problems. They thought most of Lila's problems were extreme versions of typical adolescent problems—and they were in many ways right about that—but they were such extreme versions that they could not be left to resolve of their own accord without serious risk of short- and longer-term physical and emotional problems. They were hesitant about FBT after starting treatment because they felt it did not focus on overall adolescent development and their role as parents of an adolescent. They thought they likely were failing as Lila's parents because otherwise what was the explanation for why she had all these problems, especially perhaps BN.

FBT for BN and BED focuses on behaviors first with parents taking the lead in partnering with their child in helping to reinstate a regular pattern of eating, eliminating the types of food available for binge eating, and intervening helpfully to prevent binge eating or purging during high-risk periods. There is no focus on cause, no discussion of how to change body image worries, or trying to re-structure/examine weight and shape concerns. To Lila's parents, focusing on behavioral change was putting the cart before the horse.

So parents with a child with BED or BN can get caught in the trap of trying to find the cause of these behaviors because they wish for a treatment that will address not only the eating issues, but also any relational or emotional and even developmental challenges that their child is facing. It is an understandable wish, but one that can only be partially fulfilled. In choosing a treatment like FBT though, studies suggest that improvements in other mental health problems like anxiety and depression occur with the resolution of binge eating and purging. How this comes about is not completely clear, but likely these improvements result from the familial support that FBT provides for the young person, the decreased shame and stress that comes from allowing parents to be of help when the young person is struggling on their own, and from the mastery over the urges to binge eat or purge that develops as parents successfully help their child to navigate overcoming them.

Lila and her parents agreed to try FBT but they struggled in early sessions with blaming each other and pointing fingers at each other as the real cause of binge eating and purging. Lila claimed her parents put too much pressure on her to get good grades and did not allow her enough freedom. Her parents blamed Lila's moodiness and surliness for her need to "eat her problems away."

At the beginning of FBT for BN and BED, the therapist must help parents and the young person focus in on disrupting these behaviors and not get lost in discussion of why the behavior is happening or how it relates to other problems the child is having. As in FBT for AN, FBT for BN and BED achieves the best results when reductions in these behaviors occur early in treatment. To help parents move past preoccupations with causation, it is important for them to remember the serious consequences of binge eating and purging behaviors to physical and emotional health like electrolyte imbalances, orthostasis and syncope, severe overweight, hypertension, and diabetes.

With the therapist's help, Lila and her parents agreed to try to work together on a common problem—getting rid of the foods that tempted her to binge eat more and to develop a supportive way to help Lila not purge when she felt strong urges to do so. Building this type of collaboration required moving away from finger pointing and blaming. As they did so, however, Lila felt more support and less anger toward her parents while her parents felt like Lila was making a sincere effort to get better.

How Focusing on the Cause of Avoidant/Restrictive Food Intake Disorder Interferes with FBT for ARFID

Toby was a 9-year-old boy whose pediatrician referred him and his parents for treatment due to his low weight and the extremely narrow range of foods he was willing to eat. Toby had never been a "good eater" and often didn't finish his meals, and when left on his own, sometimes did not remember to eat his lunch or snacks. He preferred to play with his friends or on his phone. Toby also had Attention Deficit Hyperactivity Disorder (ADHD) and took medications that likely also increased his baseline lack of appetite. Toby's parents were worried about his nutrition and health, but had "given up" trying to get him to eat more or different foods because it only lead to more conflicts with little change in Toby's eating. They were also concerned about his relatively poor school performance and worried about the long-term implications if that continued. His parents were unsure how to help Toby unless they understood the cause of his lack of interest in food or eating. They felt for sure it was biological because it had been present since early childhood. They requested a full gastrointestinal work-up but nothing definitive came from that.

Unlike parents with children who develop AN, BN, or BED, parents whose children have ARFID have often had a long history of observing disturbed eating patterns in their child—often since very early childhood. They have also often been told to "make your child eat" or alternatively, "don't get into food fights." These sorts of well-meaning notions have often lead to confusion, guilt, and a sense of failure on the parents' part. Since many cases of ARFID eating problems begin so early in life, there is sometimes the strong belief that there *must* be a biological explanation and/or something they did as parents when introducing foods or during feeding that *caused* these eating problems. Many parents of children with ARFID spend many years on a largely fruitless quest to find the cause and spend much time and many resources getting medical tests and procedures. Other parents focus on other problems that the child has as the cause of ARFID—such as Autism Spectrum Disorder (ASD) or ADHD. While it is true that many children with ARFID also have these other problems, most children with ASD and ADHD do not have ARFID, and these diagnoses—though they may contribute to ARFID symptoms and behaviors—cannot be accurately seen as the cause of the eating disorder. However, focusing on these other "causes" can actually distract parents from taking on the eating problems that characterize ARFID. Sometimes parents "excuse" the eating problems because these other problems take the primary focus of their time and energy. These perspectives are understandable, but can keep parents from actually tackling the ARFID symptoms and can unintentionally perpetuate and worsen the impact of ARFID on their child's growth, overall health, and social and emotional development.

It is helpful for parents of children with ARFID who embark on a course of FBT to "step back" from their focus on cause—whether in pursuit of a medical basis for the disorder or focusing on other co-morbid contributors to the symptoms of ARFID. To step back like this requires taking a bit of a leap of faith in FBT for these parents who are often weary and a bit battle worn. Parents need to find their way back to their own sense of competency and belief in their skills as parents that FBT depends on for treatment effectiveness.

Toby complained to his parents that he was often too tired to go to hockey practice and his teachers observed he was more inattentive and irritable as the day progressed, especially if he had not eaten his snacks or lunch. The therapist noted that the *cause* of Toby's easy fatigue and his inattentiveness and irritability was at least in part due to not eating enough, being underweight, and not eating a healthy diet. So, she encouraged his parents to work on that clearly relevant cause because that one can actually be mitigated in treatment. Although Toby's parents were skeptical that they could be effective in helping Toby to eat more, eat more regularly, and eat a healthier range of foods, they were surprised when they actually laid out specific goals and plans and it was helpful. In addition, Toby was rewarded for his suggestions, effort, participation, and real improvements. Getting practical about what to do and giving up on focusing on cause gave his parents the freedom to help him.

This chapter illustrates how easy it is to get off on the wrong foot in FBT for eating disorders by being overly concerned or focused on causation. Too much emphasis on why the eating problem developed keeps parents from taking action quickly and effectively and may lead to worsening symptoms and poorer outcomes. Scientific researchers will continue to work to find the cause of eating disorders, and perhaps when we better understand such causes this will help us find new and more effective treatments, but for now, parents can be helpful to their child with an eating disorder by finding ways to address the problematic behaviors rather than worrying about why the behaviors developed in the first place.

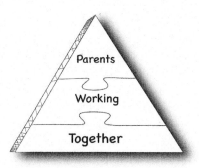

Figure 3.1 Working together: When we are in a lifeboat, we all need to row together
Nandini Datta

3
Working Together: When we are in a lifeboat, we all need to row together

> Oh, just leave her alone, she's had enough! I'm sick of her arguing and saying she doesn't want another bite, let's just leave it. Look how distressed she is. I don't think she needs one more bite, she's had enough.
>
> Parent of a child with an eating disorder

One of the core tenets emphasized early on in FBT and throughout treatment is the need for parents to work together. Eating disorders put stress on all members of the family—not just the young person with the illness. This is why it is so important that: 1) all family members attend FBT sessions; and that 2) parents and families present a united front when trying to disrupt the behaviors that keep the eating disorder in place. One thing parents soon realize is that having an eating disorder can change your child from one who is trusting to one who is sneaky and deceptive. In the service of the eating disorder, your child may utilize a range of tactics to preserve the behaviors that perpetuate the health consequences of having an eating disorder. One tactic that sometimes works is trying to split parental efforts. One parent may be perceived as more sympathetic or less likely to enforce behavioral change.

DOI: 10.4324/9781003353041-4

This "weak link" may unintentionally align with the eating disorder or give in more easily because they think they are helping their child cope with their distress. When this happens, parents may feel—in those understandably fraught moments of tension—they are supporting their child, and sometimes feel themselves unable to tolerate the distress their child is facing. This may leave the other parent perceived as being the "bad guy" and saddled with the burden of trying to mitigate dysfunctional eating behaviors alone. Unfortunately, especially during early stages of treatment, when parents may not yet be working together, it may reinforce tantrums at meals, crying, hiding, screaming, and ultimately make them more difficult to change. What might parents expect at the next meal? That's right—more of the same.

One of the things repeatedly emphasized throughout FBT is that parents need to be on the same page, the same line, the same *word*—even on the same *letter* in the word—when taking on trying to help their child battle their eating disorder. Even if parents disagree about everything else in their life or relationship, they need to find a way to agree on developing an approach together that will stop the ongoing disruptive behaviors that characterize eating disorders to minimize their impact on their child's health and well-being. This unity and alignment is integral to helping bolster re-nourishment efforts. For example, imagine a family dinner where parents are serving their ill son's meal. Imagine that in one scenario parents are debating over how much to give, how many scoops of mashed potatoes, whether or not it will upset him, and whether to put a pat of butter on it. In this scenario, this discussion is happening at the dinner table in front of the young person with an eating disorder. Most likely, the child's eating concerns will cause him to get involved in this argument, siding slyly with the parent who is questioning giving more potatoes and butter to avoid causing distress at that meal. And immediately, we have a good-parent/bad-parent scenario, and the only winner in this scenario is the eating disorder.

Sometimes one of the hardest tasks we ask parents to do in FBT is to be aligned with whomever their feeding partner is. Whether parents are married, divorced, doing this with another feeding partner (like a grandparent), the fact is that people are usually not absolutely aligned with the people they are working with all the time. That is completely understandable. We are human, after all! This is why, especially in the beginning of FBT, it is so helpful for parents to obtain real-time, *in vivo* experience learning where differences may lie and how to prioritize alignment. This is one of the reasons there is a family meal during session 2 of FBT. Meals in the beginning of FBT might be fraught with conflict and emotional distress (from all involved)—more so if you are doing a good job putting the pressure on to change dysfunctional eating. This is why it is especially important to work together with your partner, supporting one another, and bringing your own unique strengths to the table to present a unified front against the ED. These initial weeks in FBT are an opportunity to learn together with your partner what works best for the both of you in order to stay aligned in the fight against eating-disordered behaviors.

There are also some strategies that are helpful in staying aligned around re-nourishment efforts. The first strategy is developing a way to share information with your partner. This means identifying strategies that allow detailed information to be shared. Some families set up shared Word documents—this may be particularly helpful in non-intact families or two-household families—so parents can log their child's eating and be (quite literally) on the same page. Some families prefer to have pen-and-paper journals or diaries to pass back and forth. Other families schedule specific times to meet, talk, and review—without their child present—so that information can be shared candidly. What should be shared is not exclusively the quantity or composition of the meals, but also what their child does and what their emotions are. In other words, descriptions of how their child struggled or if and how things seem to be going more smoothly and with less conflict and distress. Examples of questions parents might want to ask one another include the following: Were there struggles with exercise? Did he purge? Was there any binge eating? Did he child try a new food? Were there conflicts or behavioral disruptions? What helped with emotions, distress, or getting through these challenges? What seemed to help or made matters worse? Sharing answers to these types of questions in an ongoing manner is of vital importance because they will help keep everyone focused on what works and helps instead of what does not work—thereby limiting unsuccessful experimentation.

Another thing to remember about alignment is that it does not mean everyone has to be engaging in re-nourishment efforts in exactly the same way. One of the reasons there is an emphasis on all family members participating in FBT is that each person brings with them a unique skillset, observational capacity, strengths, and coping strategies. Parents and their re-nourishment partner do not need to have the exact same approach; rather, they simply need to be on the same page about what they are doing. In some families, one parent may have historically been more in charge of taking care of family meals—prepping, shopping, cooking. In others, maybe these responsibilities were divided. Because of this, sometimes in treatment for the parent who has been previously less involved in meals becoming a more active participant can be helpful. On the other hand, sometimes it is much easier for the person who has experience and expertise in mealtimes to continue in that role, but others can step in to help rather than take over.

Other ideas to emphasize alignment can include being in agreement on the types of behaviors parents would like to see increase in their family. This can include increasing specific types of calorie-dense foods, decreasing exercise, shortening how long a meal takes, or deciding together how to get through eating disorder driven temper tantrums. Regardless of what is decided as the target problem parents want to work on, it's important to consistently work together to achieve necessary changes until the behavior is very nearly gone or at least manageable, and make sure both partners are on the same page about what they are doing and why they are doing it.

As parents progress through FBT they may notice that it sometimes becomes harder to stay aligned over time. This is because each parent may notice or focus on different eating disorder symptoms, have different opinions about how things are progressing, and have different priorities as to the child's needs as they get healthier. One thing we see often is parents having disagreements about things like the following: when to add a favorite sport back in, or how to get back to things like various after-school extracurricular activities such as sports, field trips, and other social events that might be stressful or involve eating without parents present. Overall, parents should be on the same page as much as possible about which activities should be reinstated, when this will happen, and how best to implement them. This often also involves discussions with the medical team overseeing physical health who can provide input and guidance while leaving decisions up to the parents.

Lastly, it is important to acknowledge that all families do not look the same, and in some cases, there may be one parent doing FBT on their own. On the one hand, it is true this parent doesn't need to worry about anyone agreeing with them every step of the way. But, on the other hand, this can be really difficult for one person alone because the treatment process is a very hard job to do with no one to help. In these scenarios, parents may consider getting help from a loved one, or a good friend, or other family members, who would be able to step in and provide support. Even if these allies do not directly help with changing eating behaviors, it is usually helpful to have external support for keeping the parent, as the sole parent doing this job, uplifted and refreshed (see Chapter 11). It can also be helpful to solicit support when there are other young siblings in the family who need monitoring or picking up from school so that all family members can lead as normal a life as possible even when there is a major challenge like overcoming an eating disorder to contend with. In these instances, it remains critical that those involved with helping the child change disordered eating are working together.

How Struggles to Stay Aligned Interfere With Progress in FBT for AN

Dalia was a 14-year-old freshman in a competitive college-preparatory high school. She began to restrict her eating after starting school. Her parents noticed rapid weight loss in a short period of time and notable concerning changes in her behavior—such as increased fatigue, excuses to avoid family dinners (citing too much homework, or needing to study), pushing food around on the plate when she did join family dinners, and lunches coming back untouched. When this was brought up to Dalia, she had loud, angry reactions, very uncharacteristic of her. Their worries heightened when the pediatrician noted concerns around Dalia having not gotten her menstrual period for the past several months and the significant drop in weight since her last checkup. The pediatrician highlighted the immediate need for intervention, to avoid hospitalization due to medical instability. The parents were referred to an FBT provider, whom they began with, much to Dalia's dismay.

Dalia's mother was a high-level investment banker but adjusted her schedule to be able to attend appointments. Dalia's father was mostly a stay-at-home parent, with a side business of selling resin products he created. He had much more flexibility—and was more consistently involved in meal preparation, planning, and grocery shopping. One of the things the FBT therapist emphasized in the very first session was the importance of being aligned throughout therapy. This meant making decisions about meals, when to eat, what to eat, how much to eat; for these decisions, the parents needed to be on the same page. Dalia's parents looked a little dubious, highlighting that Dalia's father was the one who did most of this, and they didn't see how altering that structure would be helpful. The therapist remained firm on the importance about parents being aligned, and tasked them with bringing a meal to the next session to re-nourish Dalia—one that they were intended to decide on together.

Dalia's parents' hesitation here is not uncommon in FBT. Sometimes parents feel like they *are* aligned, or that they have a good routine figured out that "works," but when getting into the details and navigating a difficult family meal with AN, they may find that they are not. Unfortunately, with Dalia's mother busy with work and only Dalia's father involved in mealtimes, there is an opportunity to "split" parents and lean on the parent that perhaps has less knowledge of what Dalia used to eat before she had an eating disorder. In Dalia's next session, the family meal, this is what happened.

The therapist watched as Dalia's father unpacked the family meal from a cooler—a mushroom casserole, which he reported was Dalia's favorite before the eating disorder, a side Greek salad with feta cheese and olives, and fresh baked cookies for dessert. The therapist asked how the family decided on this meal, to which Dalia's mother shrugged and stated that she left these decisions to Dalia's father and hadn't known what was being brought as she came straight from work. The therapist gently reminded the family that it is helpful if both parents are involved in these mealtime decisions, otherwise it is hard for them to support each other as they try to insist on Dalia eating enough to gain the necessary weight. As the meal progressed, the therapist asked both parents actively to share in all decisions around what food was to be eaten and how much was enough. Dalia had progressed through the dressing-less leaves of her salad and had not touched the casserole, dessert, feta, or olives. As parents jointly put pressure on Dalia to have a bite of the casserole, Dalia began to plead with her mother, viewing her as the "weaker link," stating that she never liked casserole, her father had no idea about what she enjoys eating, and will she please just "tell Dad to back off, [Mom] knows I hate the casserole!" She emphasized that if her mother had helped make the family meal decision, she never would have picked anything "as nasty as a casserole." Dalia's mother looked bewildered, her father looked defeated, and the therapist took this opportunity to again highlight the importance of parents being aligned around re-nourishment efforts. Together, they needed to make these decisions and present a united front against the eating disorder, so there would be no room for bargaining, splitting, and siding with one parent over the other. Parents nodded solemnly, having now witnessed first-hand the importance of alignment.

Dalia's parents learned an important lesson in this family meal and witnessed how quickly a young person whose thinking has been taken over by fears of weight gain because of their AN may try to divide parents to keep them from insisting on her eating.

During the rest of FBT, the parents made conscious efforts to check in with each other, working with and adapting their existing schedules to incorporate this. They set aside time before Dalia's mom left for work to come up with a meal plan for the day, so they were both on the same page about what Dalia would be expected to eat. Dalia's mom came home earlier than usual from work to prioritize family dinners and made sure to have breakfast earlier so everyone could eat at the table together. In Dalia's last few sessions, she disclosed something important to her therapist during their individual time that the therapist encouraged her to share with her parents. She stated that initially, when her parents were disconnected around the plan and what she should be eating or having more of, she felt compelled by her worries about gaining weight to look for opportunities to distract and "get away with" not eating. As her parents began to work together and meals became a standard, with no room for negotiations or bargaining, Dalia reported a strange sense of relief. She knew there was no room for her AN compulsions and fears to fight or struggle, and that she had to get through the meal. While this was initially very difficult for her because her AN-based fears were so intense at the beginning of treatment, she ultimately felt it got easier when there were fewer opportunities for her eating-disordered worries to be reinforced by successful attempts at avoiding eating.

How Struggles to Stay Aligned Interfere With Progress in FBT for BN

Praveen was a 16-year-old sophomore, and a top wrestler on his high school's competitive team. Praveen's parents were divorced, and he spent weekends with his father and weekdays with his mother. Both parents noted that he had been trying to get to a lower weight class for wrestling and engaging in different behaviors that they found a little concerning. For instance, his mother noticed he would wake up an hour early and go on a run before breakfast, and would often skip breakfast altogether, stating he "didn't have time." He'd spend time after school in the weight room and would wear heavy layers to try to "sweat off" the weight. At the end of the day, she noticed that Praveen would take several plates of food up to his room and eat large amounts of food—they found the stack of empty plates after he went to bed. On weekends, his father noticed he would spend most of the day exercising, even when he wasn't feeling well, and in once instance, when he had a sprained ankle. During one wrestling match, Praveen fainted, and his father took him to his pediatrician to get evaluated. The pediatrician found Praveen's vital signs, history of eating, and exercise behaviors very concerning and referred Praveen and his parents to an FBT clinician for Bulimia Nervosa. Praveen's parents were worried about how they would engage in family therapy because of the divorce but were concerned about Praveen's health. However, Praveen's father in particular was eager for him to get back to his sport—as was Praveen.

Divorced families can utilize FBT to help their children. Research shows that although FBT may take longer with divorced parents, they can achieve the same improvements in their children as married parents. In this vignette, both parents were appropriately concerned for Praveen and his health and well-being, but there may have been differing perspectives on how Praveen's wrestling should be managed during FBT given his father's wish to encourage Praveen to return to his sport as soon as he saw initial improvement.

After a few weeks of parental support in preventing binge eating, Praveen began to reduce this behavior, but he did not have medical clearance for exercise. He was anxious to get back to his sport. The parents were divided on how to proceed. His mother felt he needed more time to show them and himself that he would not return to binge eating and over-exercising to purge away calories. She was concerned in part because he initially developed bulimia to try to meet the weight for a lower weight class. However, his father thought he was "recovered enough" and didn't want him to lose out on the opportunity to compete in matches and enhance his chances of a wrestling scholarship. Praveen himself kept saying he felt his muscles "wasting away" and insisted that his father understood this and that he needed to get back to his sport. This often led to arguments in and out of session, between all three of the family members. Praveen's doctor had expressed enthusiasm at his progress, and while his therapist had a more cautiously optimistic approach, the overall message from both providers was to "go slow, adding activity back in very carefully." However, Praveen's parents' differing interpretations of this clinical information made it easier for his eating disorder to split parents—making his father the supportive and understanding parent and his mother the one lacking in sympathy and being unnecessarily cautious. This splitting was exacerbated by BN-driven tantrums making it harder for Praveen's parents to work together to make sure he was not bingeing or over-exercising. One of the strategies the therapist encouraged the parents to engage in was to look at clearance for activity from both a medical and behavioral perspective. Would Praveen have been *this* distraught before the eating disorder if he needed to take a break from his sport to recover from a bad cold or the flu? Would it have resulted in this much distress? Or did this feel more eating disorder driven? Praveen slumped into his chair feeling defeated, while his parents discussed together what specific behaviors they would evaluate for improvement in order for them *both* to agree that Praveen was ready to return to wrestling. Once they were on the same page, holding the same firm line against adding back activity at the moment, they noticed that Praveen's tantrums around getting back to his sport subsided and they were able to refocus on improving his behavioral progress.

In this vignette, we see two areas where parental alignment—or being on the same page—wasn't occurring. First, Praveen's parents were not aligned in when to return to wrestling, which promoted splitting and behavioral retrenchment and resistance. Second, the parents were each focusing on different aspects of the clinical information provided by their clinicians and selectively attending to those that supported their own perspective. Praveen's father heard that his son was doing well and was medically cleared to go back to his sport. Praveen's mother heard that Praveen still had significant concerns about his weight and that his ability to resist binge eating and over-exercise purging was still tentative. Both parents were partially correct and here, the therapist helped shed light on not only weight progress, which Praveen had been making, but also suggested a balanced perspective that incorporated something of what each parent valued, allowing each parent to consider the other's perspective. Ultimately, this allowed them to agree on aiming for a return to wrestling, but only when they were both confident in Praveen's behavioral progress. Once misalignment was identified and resolved, Praveen began to make progress again—and *did* get back to his sport—gradually and slowly after he had maintained a healthy weight and demonstrated consistent reduction of eating disorder behaviors, a plan both parents agreed on.

How Struggles to Stay Aligned Interfere With Progress in FBT for ARFID

Sylvie was a 6-year-old girl with a longstanding history of low appetite and lack of interest in eating. More recently, since losing her first tooth, she had begun to display a preference for soft, bland foods and sensory sensitivity around the temperature and texture of previously preferred foods. Sylvie was also diagnosed with Attention Deficit Hyperactivity Disorder (ADHD) and was on medication to help with focus on schoolwork. Her pediatrician had brought up concerns that she was rapidly losing weight with a significant change in the trajectory of her weight on her growth chart, and recommended that Sylvie's mom consider FBT for ARFID. Sylvie's mom was a single parent, who was caring for both Sylvie and her younger brother (a toddler). She felt very overwhelmed at the thought of FBT, particularly at the daunting task of re-nourishing her child without the support of another caregiver. In the first FBT session, the therapist asked if there was another adult that could help support the process. Sylvie's mom shared that her mother, Sylvie's grandmother, lived a few hours away and would be willing to come stay with the family to help. The therapist supported this plan and Sylvie's grandmother began to join sessions to learn more about behavioral strategies to help increase Sylvie's eating repertoire. Given that Sylvie's mother worked during the day, one early difficulty in treatment that arose was being on the same page about what Sylvie had eaten with her grandmother, and what strategies had been tracked and trialed. The lack of initial consistency here was confusing for both caregivers, and Sylvie herself had more conflict and confusion around mealtimes. The therapist told Sylvie and her mother that many families found that a shared chart for tracking meal progress helped with communication. They agreed and hung a chart on the refrigerator, so everyone could see what was happening for the meals. The therapist also suggested that Sylvie's mother and grandmother set aside some time for just the two of them to touch base on how the meals went using the chart as a vehicle for discussion. This way, not only was communication enabled, but they could also provide support for one another. Another area where there was some conflict between Sylvie's mother and grandmother was how best to help with her ADHD symptoms at mealtimes. Sylvie said she often felt "bored," repeatedly insisting she was full and leaving the table. Her grandmother was permissive of this behavior, wanting to listen to her claims of being full. On the other hand, her mother felt they could not rely on Sylvie's sense of satiation and that claiming fullness was Sylvie's way of getting out of finishing her meal.

Whether families are intact, in separate households, or using the support of extended family (as in Sylvie's case), it can be quite helpful to have a shared strategy to keep track of eating. It is rare that both caregivers can be at home for every meal together, making staying on the same page a little more difficult. It may require types of communication that parents haven't had to do in some time, and as shown in Sylvie's case, it is important to make sure that consistent communication occurs. For a young child with ARFID, eating new foods or trying to increase quantity can feel scary and overwhelming. Here, having both caregivers in agreement on what the plan is and presenting meals in a calm, united front can help reduce mealtime conflict while setting clear, previously agreed upon meal consumption expectations. In Sylvie's case, ADHD complicated her ability to tolerate longer mealtimes—and she became distracted and irritable. This made it all the harder to help Sylvie.

The FBT therapist encouraged Sylvie's grandmother and mother to talk together about how best to manage symptoms of inattention and hyperactivity during meals. She asked questions, and fostered discussion—modeling to both Sylvie's mother and grandmother how effective communication can be to coming up with a plan—eliminating arguments between the two of them at the dinner table. Sylvie's mother and grandmother agreed that Sylvie had to stay at the dinner table but could earn screen time for every bite she took. They also decided to read a book together throughout the meal to keep her focused.

As treatment progressed, Sylvie's mother and grandmother got into a consistent pattern of communicating, making the most of family meals (usually dinner), and figuring out a routine with Sylvie's baby brother. One of Sylvie's mother's biggest worries was whether or not he might pick up on Sylvie's eating behaviors, and she had a desire to keep the kids apart when they were eating. Sylvie's grandmother felt as though that was too difficult, as one of the two of them would need to mind the little brother and miss out on the family meal. During the family picnic (the in-session meal observation) the therapist noted that Sylvie was in fact quite delighted and distracted by her younger brother being playful with his food, the way toddlers are. The therapist pointed this out and suggested that Sylvie's mother and grandmother might consider coming up with a plan on what meals may look like. Together, Sylvie's mother and grandmother weighed the pros and cons, and decided that they would feed the toddler the bulk of his meal prior to dinner, so that the focus of the family meal could be on Sylvie's eating. This way, Sylvie's mother felt better that her son was done eating a sufficient amount, and Sylvie's grandmother could be present at the family meal. Moreover, they both agreed that Sylvie seemed happier when her brother was at meals and could laugh and giggle with him and be distracted.

Sylvie's family illustrates how challenging it can be to be aligned when working on behavioral change, but how little steps like sharing information, taking time to communicate, and identifying and coming to agreement about how to solve challenging behaviors make it possible to overcome divisiveness. Though there may be arguments and disagreements on how to proceed and who to have at meals, joint, collaborative discussion is integral in remaining united and for both parties to move forward in the treatment, feeling confident about the choices.

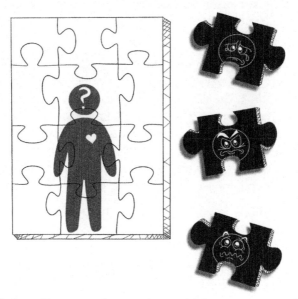

Figure 4.1 Big feelings: How too much worry about a child's emotions can undermine success
Nandini Datta

4
Big Feelings: How too much worry about a child's emotions can undermine success

> I will NOT eat this cookie! I would rather DIE!! You can't make me do it. I HATE YOU—YOU ARE THE WORST PARENT EVER! What parent makes their child eat a cookie? I never want to talk to you EVER AGAIN!

Sound familiar? At some point during treatment and recovery, it is likely that parents may encounter a similar sentiment being expressed by their child. There may be strong emotions, strong attitudes, or even strong language coming from the young person. This can be very surprising and shocking for

DOI: 10.4324/9781003353041-5

lots of parents. *Who is this person? This can't be MY child.* In this chapter we try to help parents understand why these "big feelings" arise, why they can confuse and challenge parents, and what parents can do to not be waylaid by them.

Why does FBT sometimes cause children to become upset? We encourage parents to expect big, loud, and strong emotions during treatment for an eating disorder. This is the norm, not the exception. And this may be especially different from how some children used to act and behave before they developed or were being treated for an eating disorder. These big feelings (and even emotional outbursts!) are often part of how eating disorders are expressed rather than thought of as an expression of normal adolescent emotionality or childhood oppositional behavior.

However—and this is important—when children express high levels of emotion, this does not mean that parents are doing a "bad job" in trying to help their child. In fact, it can often indicate the opposite. It may mean that they are being effective in disrupting behaviors that are maintaining the eating disorder—especially when the emotional upset is related to eating or eating-related behaviors. Challenging these behaviors almost by necessity causes some emotional responses—usually negative ones—which is why parents are likely to notice big reactions from their child at times, particularly before, during, and after meal/snack times. That is why it is important to develop tools and strategies in consultation with the FBT therapist to help children (and parents!) more effectively manage these strong emotions.

It may help to think about it this way—imagine cleaning a room in a home. This involves sorting through closets with years of untouched, unidentifiable stuff, random boxes, and who even knows what this is under the bed? In order to sort through all the items, remove what is not wanted, decide what is no longer needed, reorganize what is left, then dust and clean—it is going to take significant time, effort, and maybe even a little sweat along the way. In the middle of this project usually the room will look *worse* before it looks better. If someone looked in during the middle of cleaning, the room might look like a tornado tore through it. This analogy may apply to a family's experience with eating disorder treatment. It might feel that everything is in disarray, turned upside down, and more confused in the middle of treatment than before it started. But to get to that nicely organized, clean room, the mess is a necessary step in the process. That is why parents are encouraged to stick with the course of treatment by consistently applying skills and strategies to disrupt eating disorder behaviors and promote health, even when emotions run high at times. When this happens, it is also not the time to add more therapists or try different approaches—those efforts will likely just add more confusion and complexity to the mix (see Chapter 7).

Try to not let "big feelings" derail recovery. Also, it can help to acknowledge just how deeply the child with an eating disorder is truly suffering. Their pain is real and valid. The fear and anxiety they feel when confronted with food, eating, or stopping a compensatory strategy is enormous. As a parent, it is tempting to want to try to step in and take away those strong negative feelings. After all, parents love their children and it is only natural to want to make their negative feelings go away and stop their suffering. However, in the case of an eating disorder, these emotions sometimes interfere with the task of bringing the child back to health, and can in turn end up reinforcing the eating disorder behaviors and thoughts. As a parent, it is imperative to find a way to respond effectively to these strong negative emotions or outbursts that are driven by the eating disorder worries by expressing sympathy and understanding to the child who is suffering, while not letting the strong emotions distract from enforcing necessary behavioral changes.

It may help to think of a common situation many parents find themselves faced with: when their child needs to be inoculated against common childhood diseases. Needles often promote fear, anxiety, worry, and dread in young children (and in older children and adults too sometimes). Yet it is often important and potentially life-saving for children to have to tolerate the pain of needles required to deliver vaccines or medications. Parents usually find ways to help their child cope with the big feelings that arise when faced with a needle, because parents understand the lasting health importance behind the temporary discomfort. Eating disorder treatment is the same. The fear and anxiety a child might feel about eating is often short-lived, and gets better with time as the child recovers. Can it be upsetting and elicit strong feelings? Yes it can, but parents need to ask themselves, do the discomfort and pain outweigh the emotional and physical health benefits that come from effective FBT treatment? Will a young person with an eating disorder become upset when asked to eat a feared food? Do the few minutes or sometimes even hours of crying and screaming outweigh lasting health benefits of full recovery from an eating disorder? If it feels too overwhelming in the moment when faced directly with these "big feelings," try zooming out and consider the long-term benefits of helping your child move past the eating disorder.

Or consider this scenario. Let's say you have severe arachnophobia. You hate spiders. Always have, always will. Now let's say you take a job at a zoo. As part of your job, you are required to care for the tarantulas in the spider habitat. This entails cleaning their cages, feeding them, and monitoring their behavior. Would you be able to do this? How would you feel on day one of the new job? Now imagine knowing you have to face your fears every day, multiple times a day. You might be tempted to quit!

This is not all that dissimilar from how a child with an eating disorder might feel at times. Eating may be just as scary to them as facing that giant hairy spider. And unlike a job or recreational habit, the child *has* to eat in order to restore their health. It is not an option not to eat. That can be a terrifying and overwhelming place to be. However, parents should not let big feelings prevent them from acting in the best interest of their child to help them recover. Expressing emotional distress is often a tactic that the eating disorder will use to disrupt progress and put off the thing (eating) that causes the anxiety or worry for the child. The research literature suggests that avoiding anxiety-provoking situations often makes them worse, not better, over time. Evidence-based treatments to help with phobias and fears involve exposure and desensitization training, and these interventions typically trigger strong emotions, but also provide opportunities for a person to gain mastery of their feelings and environment through repeated learning experiences. For someone with an eating disorder, eating in itself is often an exposure. The emotional responses a child feels can be strong, yet these feelings are expected and part of the healing process. If the child were to stop eating (and thereby stop exposing themselves to the fear), this likely would leave the eating disorder behaviors unchallenged and make the child much sicker over time.

Sometimes the only way to make it past the fear is to face the fear. And keep in mind that while the fear associated with eating and/or weight restoration may not be based in reality, it still will *feel* very real in the moment to the person who is afraid. The eating disorder can cloud their judgment and not let them recognize that the fear is irrational. But parents can signal to the healthy part of their child that there is nothing to fear by continuing on with treatment goals and supporting them in overcoming the very thing that makes them so anxious. Here are some helpful suggestions to try when emotions are high: 1) distraction, taking a short break from the task at hand; 2) thinking about a future goal, deep breathing; 3) staying calm, changing the topic; 4) taking a "time out" from the conversation, acknowledging and validating the emotions; 5) providing comfort in the way each child receives it best; and 6) engaging in self-care for yourself and your child.

What happens when "big feelings" come to therapy? One additional note about "big feelings"—sometimes these emotions will be outwardly expressed during FBT sessions. It is common for children and adolescents with eating disorders to experience difficulty regulating their emotions during treatment sessions. This does *not* mean that FBT is not working. Nor does this mean that the child needs to meet with a different FBT therapist or seek alternative forms of eating disorder treatment. Occasionally, the eating disorder concerns the child has will lead to using emotional outbursts or reports of how much they dislike treatment to convince parents to try a different treatment approach (or none at all). Or parents may feel that they need to find a different therapist that their child can better connect with so the child's feelings will be less upset in order for FBT to be successful. These are myths that have not panned out in the research. In fact, engaging in treatment switching and therapist shopping behaviors often results in the eating disorder symptoms getting stronger and more difficult to treat, as care is delayed and no real movement is made towards treatment goals during this time. FBT therapists have likely seen exactly this situation before and can provide additional guidance on how to proceed. Stay the course with treatment and weather the storm together with the support team.

What about self-harm and suicidal ideation? It is not uncommon for children and adolescents to express strong emotions through statements that suggest harm. The only thing that trumps sticking with highly focused eating disorder treatment goals is active, acute suicidality. Statements from a child of wanting to harm or kill themselves should *always* be taken with the utmost sincerity and quick, supportive action from parents and/or treatment providers. However, not all of these statements or behaviors should be seen as the time to stop FBT. These kinds of statements and behaviors can be ways to disrupt efforts in re-nourishment by threatening self-harm. At times, the eating disorder can use this as a "big emotion" to stop parents in FBT. If caught off guard, this can be a very effective technique in preventing parents from helping their child progress with recovery goals. For example, parents may feel hesitant to provide adequate nutrition to their child if they feel doing so might cause their child to act in a way to harm themselves. Or they may give in to the eating disorder demands in order to keep the peace and not upset their child. Below is an example of how fears of their child harming themselves or threatening suicide can keep AN behaviors in place and almost derail FBT.

Alice was a 14-year-old female with AN and depression. Prior to being diagnosed with AN and starting FBT, Alice lost 18 pounds and began experiencing physical symptoms of malnourishment, such as a slow heart rate (bradycardia) and fainting spells. Upon starting FBT, her parents took over preparing and plating meals, and helped Alice gain 10 pounds. However, due to concerns about Alice's low mood, the parents were fearful of pushing Alice too hard and chose to re-nourish her based only on Alice's "safe foods." After consultation with their FBT therapist, her parents decided to ask Alice to have pasta again. Alice had not eaten pasta in over a year and remained fearful of re-introducing carbohydrates. See below for how the session went:

Therapist: Parents—you've done a terrific job of working together and preparing meals to help Alice gain weight and improve her health. Are there any foods that still seem to be challenging for Alice to eat?

Mom: Well I have noticed one food in particular...

Alice: Mom! Stop! I eat SO much food right now! I'm eating everything you give me! Why do we even need to have this conversation?

Mom: Sweetie, the doctor asked if you are struggling with any foods, and it's true—you are doing a great job eating the meals we make you. It's just that we make you the same thing over and over again.

Alice: What's wrong with that? Lots of people eat the same thing all the time!

Mom: Yes, and there's still some nights where I make a separate dinner for you because I know you won't eat what the rest of the family is having.

Dad: Yes, I've noticed this too. My wife makes the best lasagna. But Alice won't touch it.

Mom: Actually, Alice has not eaten pasta of any kind since the AN started.

Therapist: Is pasta something you both would like Alice to try?

Mom: Yes, that would be great...

Alice [interrupting]: No—no way. I am not going to eat lasagna. Pasta is SO unhealthy for you! I stopped eating pasta a year ago. It's full of carbohydrates and it's gross.

Mom: Alice always gets so upset when we ask her to eat pasta.

Dad: That's an understatement. Remember what happened last time?

Therapist: What happened? Can someone explain a bit more?

Mom: Well, last Friday night I made spaghetti for the family. I plated a very small portion for Alice because I know that she gets really mad when we ask her to eat pasta. She refused to eat it, started screaming at the dinner table about how unhealthy it was, and threatened to hurt herself if we made her eat it.

Alice: You never give me pasta. You know I don't like it. I don't understand why you are making me eat something that I hate. Who does that?

Therapist: Oh, I see. Mom/Dad—what did you do next?

Dad: Well Alice got so upset that she threatened to run away if we forced her to eat it. At one point, she said she would rather die than eat the pasta. That made us pretty scared. We don't ever want to make her do anything to hurt herself, so we replaced the pasta with an apple, which seemed to help calm the situation.

Mom: Exactly. If Alice is gaining weight with the foods she wants to eat right now, I am not sure why we need to make her eat pasta. Her mood is already so low that we don't want to do anything to make her feel worse.

Therapist: It sounds like that dinner was a very scary and stressful experience for everyone. It also sounds like AN is worried about eating pasta, which is why you saw such big emotions from Alice during that dinner. Mom/Dad—there was an important reason why you asked Alice to eat the spaghetti. This is a typical dinner for your family and AN has convinced Alice that pasta is a food to be feared. It makes sense that you would want to help her overcome that at this stage in treatment. Mom/Dad—do you have a plan to help support Alice in staying safe while also not giving into the eating disorder's food preferences?

Mom: Not really. I guess we need to make a plan in case this happens again. I'm worried about asking her to eat pasta again. We want to keep our daughter safe. As you know, she struggles with depression and low mood, and I just don't want to make things worse. She's already been through so much and always seems so sad.

This is a natural response that any loving caretaker would have. However, it can be very problematic in FBT for parents to back off from helping re-nourish their child. It is recommended that parents develop a plan, in consultation with their FBT provider, on how to manage concerns about self-harm and suicidality should they arise in their child at any point during treatment.

FBT providers will be thoughtful about these concerns and will assess for suicidal ideation and evaluate self-harm throughout treatment. As parents, it will be important to stay vigilant towards these concerns and have a plan ahead of time in case a child starts to express suicidal ideation. Remember— asking and talking about suicidal ideation does *not* increase someone's likelihood of engaging in a behavior to hurt themselves. Do not be worried about asking about these feelings or seeking out support from the treatment team if concerned. The treatment team may recommend taking the child to the nearest hospital or emergency medicine center for an evaluation. This step should not be viewed as a last resort option and should be seen as one tool parents have in their toolbox to keep their child safe. Trained medical and mental health professionals can then evaluate the situation, assess for safety, and help create a plan. Again, all statements of self-harm or suicidal ideation should be taken very seriously, evaluated immediately, and appropriate action taken to ensure safety above all else.

One hallmark feature of FBT is the use of weekly weighing and a weight chart to track progress. In the case of AN and BN in particular, weighing and weight gain can sometimes cause emotional struggles because of the fear and anxiety these elicit in children with eating disorders. Some parents (and some clinicians) try to help children by weighing them blindly (not letting them see their weight) so the child will not become distressed. The problem with this is that the young person needs to tolerate this experience and learn to manage this distress, not avoid it. Fears cannot be overcome by avoiding them, especially fears about necessary aspects of life, like eating and weighing enough to be healthy. Gradually exposing young people who are afraid of weight gain to their weight progress by sharing it with them and supporting them when they are distressed helps them gain mastery of their fears. That is one reason FBT requires weighing and discusses weight gain in front of the young person. While some parents may want to protect their child from their distress and fears, keeping their weights from them only delays the ultimate need for them to know their weights and may actually worsen the child's anxiety rather than contain it. The short-term avoidance of distress is not worth the loss of the longer-term benefits of gradually desensitizing and normalizing of weight gain. Parents sometimes struggle with this, but it is important to understand why it is necessary and how it is ultimately helpful, even if it can be emotionally upsetting for their child.

Combatting disordered eating in a child can lead to parents also having strong emotions and some struggle to manage them. Parents may feel more short-tempered, frustrated, annoyed, sad, or worried than usual. This may be directed at their child, partner, other family members, coworkers or friends. It may be particularly challenging to keep up with everyday work demands and family obligations. Helping a child recover from an eating disorder is hard work! Be sure to engage in self-care strategies along the way. How can a parent best get help for their own emotional distress? First, do not be afraid to ask others for help. *What do you need from your partner right now? Can your neighbor pick up the kids from sports practice? Does your house REALLY need to be vacuumed this week? Will anyone notice if you do not volunteer to coordinate the school fundraiser this year?* It is also important to find creative ways to pre-serve time and energy while in the first phase of FBT. Parents need to support each other and step in to help when their co-parent needs some help (see Chapter 3 and Chapter 11). Many parents find the first phase of FBT the hardest due to the time required to monitor their child's eating behaviors as well as the "big feelings" that often arise in their child when they first start treatment.

Sometimes, big feelings may outwardly look small. Particularly at the start of treatment, children and adolescents may appear to be OK with increasing intake, gaining weight, trying new foods, or stopping exercise behaviors, but on the inside the exact opposite is happening. Some youths with eating disorders want to please parents and providers and can actu-ally appear to be doing quite well on the surface with recovery-oriented goals. This is sometimes referred to as the "swan swim"—the swan appears to be gliding along the water effortlessly, but just underneath the surface, there is a flurry of frenzied activity with webbed feet to keep the swan in motion and moving forward. Young people with ED may be able to engage in their own kind of "swan swim." They might obey and comply with parent wishes, and may even regain weight or stop ED behaviors quickly, to avoid conflict or disappointing their loved ones. It is some-times not until the middle of treatment or phase 2 when the young person expresses or displays their distress. Particularly when the child must now battle the ED thoughts more independently as they regain responsibility for eating and engaging in social eating activities. Again, this is not a sign to stop treatment or that FBT is not working. Rather, it is important to understand that the child may have experienced these feelings all along and work together to help effectively regulate strong emotions while also progressing on treatment goals.

Here are just a few examples of how big feelings and emotional reactions showed up in the course of FBT and the strategies families found to help them through it.

How Big Feelings Can Interfere With FBT for AN

Deepika was a 15-year-old Indian American female. She presented to FBT with her married parents and 13-year-old brother. Prior to starting FBT, Deepika reported experiencing symptoms of AN for about one and a half years, but was only recently diagnosed after concern about her health and mood were mentioned by her teachers. After undergoing an evaluation and receiving a diagnosis of AN, the family began FBT. Deepika was restricting across all meals, refusing to eat the food prepared by her family, and often skipping meals or fasting for more than 24 hours at a time. Deepika needed approximately 20 pounds of weight gain to restore health. Throughout treatment, Deepika was closely medically monitored and inpatient hospital admission for her medical health was considered several times. However, Deepika did not require hospitalization and was able to maintain treatment progress on an outpatient basis.

Deepika had significant difficulty tolerating FBT sessions. She would often yell and scream at her parents as well as the FBT therapist. She would call her mother obscene names. Outside of session, her parents reported that Deepika would throw away the food prepared for her, would refuse to come out of her room, and argued constantly with her parents even outside of mealtimes. On several occasions, Deepika became so upset that she threatened to run away or jump off the roof of their house. Her parents had to physically block the exits to prevent Deepika from acting on these thoughts more than once. Sessions were often chaotic and involved lots of screaming, swearing, and crying.

The FBT therapist helped the parents understand that these in-session disruptions were one way in which the eating disorder tried to delay care and focus the family away from the task of re-nourishment due to the fear of associated weight gain. The family could have easily become distracted or tempted to use the sessions to help regulate Deepika's behaviors. Instead, the family made appropriate plans with the therapist regarding safety (both in and outside of session), stayed the course, persisted with the re-nourishment tasks, and restored weight within the first phase of FBT. She started eating pizza and even requesting takeout foods, which had not happened since before her AN developed. Her relationship with her brother improved and parents noticed less resistance during meal/snack times. Deepika had difficulty with the transition of independence around food and eating during phase 2 and continued to experience a high level of emotional dysregulation as well as withdrawal, isolation, and sadness. The parents and FBT therapist remained concerned about her mood symptoms. After discharging from FBT, the family decided that a Dialectical Behavioral Therapy approach through an intensive out-patient program was the next best step to support Deepika's emotional and mental health needs.

The case above illustrates the progress that a family and patient can make despite big feelings and difficulty regulating emotions. Had the parents decided to stop FBT and pursue alternative treatments for the patient's behavioral outbursts, it could have significantly delayed her progress with recovery from AN and potentially endangered her life. The family was able to prioritize her medical needs for nutrition and medical stability first, then sought out support for her remaining mood symptoms and emotional regulation difficulties. It would have been understandable if the family thought they should stop FBT or consider a different approach, given just how concerning the patient's behaviors were when asked to eat. Yet, the family understood that these reactions were coming from the illness—not the patient herself—and decided to push forward in service of treating her AN and saving her life. Although research suggests that mood symptoms, such as anxiety and depression, often improve following the resolution of an eating disorder, they may not completely resolve particularly if the mood disorder pre-dated the start of the eating disorder. As such, patients may need additional treatment focused on improving anxiety and/or depression symptoms after completing FBT. These concerns should be discussed with the FBT therapist who can help families prioritize life-threatening treatment targets and provide recommendations for further psychiatric care, if needed.

How Big Feelings Can Interfere With FBT for Binge Eating and BN

Charlie was a 14-year-old Korean American transgender female with approximately a one-year history of binge eating and purging behaviors. She attended FBT with her married parents and two younger brothers. Prior to starting FBT, Charlie would often skip meals to try to restrict intake and lose weight. As part of her treatment, Charlie's parents decided to have family breakfast and dinners to help promote a regular meal pattern for Charlie. This change prompted a strong negative reaction from Charlie. Her parents reported that Charlie would refuse to eat and storm off to her room. These behaviors upset everyone, including Charlie's younger siblings, and made mealtimes stressful for everyone in the family. After two days of insisting on family meals, Charlie's parents decided to allow her to eat in her room alone again, as she had done prior to starting FBT, because they wanted to "keep the peace at home."

In the next FBT session, Charlie reported continuing to skip meals, which then would often lead to a late-night binge episode, followed by vomiting before bed. It was clear that Charlie needed more support given how strong the eating disorder behaviors were. Charlie's FBT therapist talked with the family about ways to increase support and monitoring, both during meals and afterwards, to help regulate Charlie's eating. Her parents shared their concerns that monitoring Charlie's meals was causing increased stress and conflict, and that they wanted to prioritize a calm family dinner environment. The FBT therapist helped explain that for many adolescents with an eating disorder, these types of outbursts are expected. The FBT therapist worked with Charlie's parents in developing a plan to help decrease conflict while also insisting on eating behaviors in line with recovery. Charlie's parents began insisting on family meals, and were not deterred from doing so even when Charlie got upset or engaged in arguments at mealtimes. Over the next few weeks, Charlie gradually began to eat more regularly throughout the day and decreased both binge eating and purging frequency.

While initially it was uncomfortable to ask their child to do something that caused distress and increased family conflict, Charlie's family worked together effectively with their therapist in understanding the importance of staying the course with FBT and not allowing "big feelings" to distract from treatment goals. Upon reflection, the family acknowledged that the short-term discomfort caused by increased yelling at mealtimes for a week or two was easily well worth it in the grand scheme of helping their child recover from an eating disorder. Although it felt hard and uncomfortable for everyone in those tense moments, Charlie's parents were ultimately glad they did not give in to the eating disorder's wishes and helped their child do what was needed to get well.

How Big Feelings Might Interfere With FBT for ARFID

Marcy was an 11-year-old white female with co-occurring ADHD and a longstanding history of ARFID. Marcy had been a picky eater since birth and struggled to add foods into her diet. Although Marcy was not underweight, there were significant concerns with her ability to expand her food preferences in order to eat with others, consume enough lunch during the school day, and maintain adequate nutrition for growth with puberty on the horizon. Marcy presented to FBT with her mother. Her parents were divorced and she spent every other weekend with her biological father. He was not interested in participating in Marcy's FBT and did not attend any sessions. Marcy was an only child and there were no stepsiblings living with either parent.

During the family meal in session 2 of FBT, Marcy became very dysregulated when asked to eat vegetable stir fry, which her mother had prepared and brought to the session. This was a food on the "never" column in Marcy's "always, sometimes, never" list. Marcy started screaming loudly, refusing to eat the new food. At one point, Marcy took the thermos container that held her food and threw it across the room at her mother, hitting her mother in the face and leaving an instant mark. Marcy was so fearful of trying the new food and so upset that she was not able to be remorseful in the moment or acknowledge that her reaction had harmed her mother. Marcy's ARFID was so strong and she was so afraid of trying the new food that she felt cornered and had limited restraint in the moment. Instead of reacting back with anger, Marcy's mother remained calm and insisted on finishing out the treatment session. The FBT therapist worked with Marcy and her mother to develop de-escalation techniques in order for Marcy to express how scared, frustrated, and upset she was while also keeping everyone—including Marcy—safe from harm. The FBT therapist made it clear that harming behaviors would not be tolerated, nor should Marcy's mother be expected just to accept the harm because Marcy had ARFID. The FBT therapist also worked with Marcy and her mother to make a plan for how to safely manage similar situations at home.

Marcy went on to complete a full course of FBT for ARFID over the next six months. She did well with treatment, adding more than ten foods to her "always" list. The FBT therapist integrated Marcy's positive response to praise and rewards into sessions, holding a "graduation" ceremony every time a food moved from the "never" to the "sometimes" and eventually the "always" columns on the list. The FBT therapist allowed Marcy to be physically active in session and provided toy-like materials to help her stay focused, engaged, and effective in regulating her emotions that arose.

FBT does not promote or condone violence in any form. Just because someone has an eating disorder does not provide them with a pass to physically injure themselves or someone else. Just as parents work to keep their child safe from harm, so too should parents find ways to protect themselves if their child acts out in a threatening or harmful manner. These behaviors do not mean that FBT is contra-indicated. Nor does it mean that now is not the "right time" to work on eating disorder treatment. However, it does mean that the family needs a plan on how to progress with treatment goals while also managing strong feelings and reactions.

FBT, as with any psychological treatment, often results in patients and families experiencing strong emotions. Therapy of any kind entails introspection and reflection, and usually involves a growth process. It is certainly not always easy and comfortable! Parents can learn to help their child effectively process their "big feelings" while also promoting eating disorder recovery.

Figure 5.1 Stop blaming your child or yourself: You're fighting an eating disorder, not your child or yourself
Nandini Datta

5
Stop Blaming Your Child or Yourself: You're fighting an eating disorder, not your child or yourself

> I don't know why she's doing this to herself. She knows better. She must take responsibility for what she's doing or it will never get better!
>
> Mother of a girl diagnosed with Bulimia Nervosa

Consider a family's experience of coming to understand that there was a fierce struggle going on inside their child between two opposing forces. The first force is their child's true, healthy self, his true wishes, and the second force is the eating disorder, with its destructive aims. As the eating disorder (ED) gets stronger, the child's true self gets weaker, and as they respond to their child's behavior the parents must think carefully about which side is *actually* being strengthened by their actions.

DOI: 10.4324/9781003353041-6

For a long time, we were angry with our son for his behaviors around food. We wanted family meals to be times when we came together to talk about the day, to share food, to make each other laugh, support each other. But our son's refusal to eat meant that mealtimes were a tense, stressful experience. There were constant arguments. Our other children didn't even want to come to the table, and when they did, they would bolt their food down in silence and get up to leave the moment they were finished. When we discovered our son had been hiding food in his pockets instead of eating it, I was so upset that I burst into tears, and my husband got really angry at him. Our other kids were angry with him too and told him he was selfish for deceiving us and for upsetting us all so much.

It was only after we learned that almost all kids with eating disorders do these kinds of things that we understood that it was the eating disorder that was causing our son to behave in ways that were totally out of character for him. Instead of thinking that he was bad, we came to realize that the eating disorder was influencing him to do things he would not normally do. Then, instead of getting angry with him, we saw that we needed to take action to protect him from this illness that was causing him to do things that were going to hurt him as well as upset us.

We wished we had realized this sooner, because afterwards we regretted that we had gotten angry with him when he was at his most vulnerable and really needed our help. And what's more, when we were angry with him for the things he did, and made him feel badly about them, it only made it harder for him to change. The worse he felt about himself, the harder he found it to resist what the ED was telling him. He needed support and understanding from all of us so that he could do what he needed to do to recover; fight back against what the ED was saying to him.

In FBT, we often talk about separating the child from the ED, or "externalizing" the eating disorder. This concept can be difficult for parents to understand, partly because we can't "see" the eating disorder in the same way we might be able to see a broken bone on an X-ray. When an illness affects any part of a child's body other than the brain, it's easier to see that the condition is separate from the child and is impacting on what they can do and how they feel. For example, a broken leg means that the child can't easily walk or run even if they try to. And from an emotional standpoint, they may be upset they can't play sports because of their injury, or they may be irritable if they are in pain. This is easy for us all to understand and empathize with.

But when an illness primarily affects mind/brain functioning, it can be much more difficult to separate the person from the illness. This is true not just for eating disorders, but also for conditions like depression or anxiety. Almost all brain-based disorders will change the way a person feels, thinks, and behaves. And mostly that effect is going to be negative. The person will likely be more difficult, rigid, irrational, argumentative, even aggressive. Mind-/brain-based disorders tend to diminish a person's capacity for reasoning, constrain their ability to consider creative solutions to problems, and restrict their ability to feel empathy. Eating disorders cause young people to feel and believe things that lead them to desperately want to engage in self-destructive behaviors, but when parents see their child actively engaging in eating disorder behaviors it can be difficult for them to understand the degree to which the eating disorder is responsible for the things their child is saying and doing. Parents may mistakenly believe their child is *choosing* to engage in behaviors, when in fact the illness is influencing the child to such a degree that the child feels *driven* to engage in behaviors. Generally, by the time the family comes to treatment, the child has already lost the capacity to make a free and rational choice about almost everything related to eating and their health.

Clinicians see many young people with eating disorders, and young people with eating disorders tend to think and behave in similar ways, so it is easier for clinicians to see diagnostic features and patterns, allowing them to separate the eating disorder from the young person. Parents, however, usually only know their own child, and they are therefore perplexed, frightened, or frustrated with their child's behaviors, seeing it as something the child is doing and not a result of an eating disorder. It is not at all uncommon for parents to feel angry with their children for their behaviors, because the behaviors are dangerous, oppositional, and generally very challenging for any family to cope with.

The reason we work so much on externalization in FBT is that we want to protect relationships in the family by helping the family to understand and empathize with the child's experiences around ED so that they can intervene more effectively to help their child recover. When parents better understand how the eating-disordered concerns are pressuring their child, it helps them to support their child in ways that are going to be more likely to lead to positive change. We sometimes find it helpful to suggest to parents to imagine that they are anthropologists, observing their child's patterns of behaviors, noting how they have changed over time, so that they can begin to see how the illness has co-opted the child's thinking and behaviors into working in the service of the eating disorder. This is the reason we encourage parents to separate the illness symptoms from their child's true values. We tell them that if their child is behaving in a way that makes no sense, or that they simply do not understand, or is very uncharacteristic, they are probably looking at something that is being caused by the eating disorder and is not part of the child's true, healthy self. We remind parents that their child doesn't actually want to be anxious and irrational and argumentative. Sometimes we say something like,

> listen to the voice that is coming out of your child's mouth, and ask yourself, is this my child's true, healthy self that is talking to me, or is this the eating disorder worries talking through my child? Is the thing my child says he wants right now going to be helpful or harmful in the long run?

Separating these things out can help parents understand that they may need to refuse their child's requests to engage in exercise or to eat only certain kinds or amounts of food, because parents absolutely must make decisions that are based on acting in the best interests of the child rather than decisions that are based on giving their child what she is asking for right now. Separating the child from the eating disorder can also help parents remember that if their child is engaging in behaviors such as lying about what they are eating, hiding food, secretly exercising, or vomiting, this doesn't mean that the child is a liar, or is manipulative, or bad. It simply means that the eating disorder is having a pernicious effect on the child's behavior, *as it does in almost every case.*

The child themselves sometimes resists the concept of externalization. For example, it often happens that when a therapist encourages parents to consider whether it is their child or the eating disorder who is saying they don't want butter on their toast, the child will become very upset, insisting that these are their true feelings. And yes, it's true that at that moment the child really does feel and believe certain things. The point, however, is that they feel and believe these things *because* they have an eating disorder. If we allow the worries the child experiences because of the eating disorder to drive their behavior choices, this will result in a great deal of harm to the their physical and mental health. It can even result in the death of the child.

FBT therapists work to help parents hear not only the voice that says that to feed them more or stop them from exercising causes them to be very upset, but also to "hear" the silenced voice of their child, which would, if it could, be saying something like,

> I'm starving, I don't want to be sick, I want to be healthy. I don't want to die. I want to live a full and normal life and be free from fear about food and "fatness." Please help me, I can't do this by myself.

No child actually wants to starve themselves to death. The child's true self wants things that are much more aligned with the kinds of things the parents also want for their child: robust physical health, resilient mental health, strong self-esteem, positive relationships with family and friends, freedom from fear, age-appropriate independence, the capacity to feel joyful.

Parents struggle with the concept of externalization for lots of different reasons. In cases of AN, typically there is a sudden and dramatic change in the child's behavior, along with significant weight loss. In these cases, parents can usually see the changes AN has brought about in their child, but they may overestimate their child's ability to turn the situation around. They expect their child to behave intelligently and rationally and reasonably, because the child has always done so. This can lead some parents to be disappointed and angry when their child does not behave in their usual and expected ways. And this response from parents can put strain on the parent–child relationship and will generally not help the child cope with the ED (see Chapter 4).

For parents of young people with BN, the onset of the disorder is usually more insidious. The binge-purge behaviors associated with the disorder are often associated with shame and the young person strives to keep the behaviors hidden from others. Weight loss may be less dramatic in BN—though the binge and purge behaviors are significantly risky in medical terms—and parents may not know how often the binge-purge behaviors are occurring. With BN, it can be harder for the parents to "see" the eating disorder and for this reason it can be harder for them to see the ways it is taking over their child's thinking and behavior.

For parents of children with ARFID, the concept of externalization can be particularly challenging. Children who have had ARFID for some time have usually had eating difficulties from their earliest years and so it can be especially difficult for their parents to separate ARFID from their child simply because there was never a time when their child behaved any differently. Also, the many years of struggle around eating often have the effect of eroding parents' confidence as well as their patience, and they have often reached a point where they feel frustrated with their child. FBT therapists work with parents of ARFID children to help them understand that all children with ARFID have similar difficulties and behavior patterns, and that their child is not being willful or difficult, but instead is struggling to cope with a condition that is not his fault and in fact is an illness. And the therapist will work to help parents remember that their child needs their help to cope with making the changes he needs in order to be healthy.

How Failing to Separate AN From the Young Person Affects FBT

When Kayla's parents, Caroline and Jack, spoke to the FBT therapist prior to their first FBT session, they explained that Kayla was diagnosed with AN and had been admitted to hospital due to low weight, but that since being discharged home she was doing better, and was gaining weight. Indeed, they said, Kayla's weight was almost back to her normal range, so they were feeling confident things were on the right track.

When the family arrived for their first FBT session, the therapist explained that she would weigh Kayla at the start of each session, and so she asked her to come along to another room for a weight check. Kayla immediately became upset, saying to her parents, "You know how much it stresses me out to be weighed and you just checked my weight two days ago and you know it's fine." Caroline seemed upset by Kayla's distress and tried to calm her down by telling the therapist that there was no need for her to check the weight again, because she had indeed weighed Kayla at home and that the weight was "fine" at 110 lb. The therapist said she nonetheless would still need to check Kayla's weight at the start of every visit. Kayla became angry then, saying, "I don't want to have to get my weight checked here. This is not supposed to be a medical visit. This is supposed to be therapy." Caroline and Jack looked at each other uncertainly, and Caroline again said to the therapist, "I have been checking her weight regularly and it's been good, so I don't think we need to check it again if it's causing her unnecessary stress." The therapist politely but firmly insisted on checking Kayla's weight, saying it was an important part of the treatment. She instructed Kayla to come along with her and said they would talk together about it.

When she was alone with Kayla, the therapist gently asked her to tell her why she was so upset about this weight check. Kayla did not reply. The therapist said she wondered whether maybe Kayla was worried the weight measure on the clinic scale was going to be quite different from the one taken at home. Kayla began to cry. The therapist tried to reassure Kayla that whatever the weight was, they would face it together, and she would work to help Kayla's parents deal with the news.

When Kayla finally stood on the scale, her weight came in at 90 lb. The therapist was not shocked, as she had an idea just from looking at Kayla that the 110 lb reported weight was unlikely to be accurate. She asked Kayla what she had done at home to get the scales to read at 110 lb. Kayla didn't reply, so the therapist gently said,

> Hey, you don't have to tell me, but your parents are probably going to be upset and they are going to ask about what has happened, and the more I know the better I can explain it to them and help them to be not quite so upset.

She gave Kayla a bit of time to think about it, but Kayla still wouldn't talk to her.

When Kayla and the therapist came back into the room to join Kayla's parents and siblings, the therapist gently explained that Kayla's weight was coming in at 90 lb. Caroline and Jack were utterly shocked. They couldn't believe the weight could be that different. In fact, they were convinced that the clinic's scales must be inaccurate. The therapist offered that one of the parents could check their own weight on the clinic scales. Caroline did that, and she saw that the scales measured her own weight accurately.

At that point, Kayla's father began to get very angry. He turned to Kayla and demanded to know how she had managed to deceive them. Kayla hung her head and refused to answer. Kayla's mother explained that she was the one who had been checking Kayla's weight, because Kayla had said it "stressed" her if her father was present at the weight check. Jack was angry he had been excluded from the process and said to Caroline, "I told you this would happen. Obviously, Kayla is able to manipulate you completely." Caroline looked stressed by her husband's criticism. She turned to the therapist, saying, "But the scales at home definitely said 110 pounds and I checked it by weighing myself too. It was accurate. I don't know what could have happened." Kayla was sitting looking at the floor. Her siblings looked away, as if they wanted to be anywhere but in that room.

The therapist worked to help the parents understand that manipulation of weights is a common behavior amongst young people with eating disorders. She asked them to imagine what they might do if they were in a situation where they might lose everything they cared about unless they could make a particular weight on a scale. She asked them to consider whether there might be situations where the stakes were so high that they just might lie, even if they were normally truthful people. However, the parents' emotions were running high, with shock and anxiety, and they struggled to hear what they therapist said.

The next week, Jack told the therapist that they had searched Kayla's bedroom and discovered that she had two 10 lb gym weights that she had been strapping to the inside of her legs under her nightdress before she stepped on to the weighing scales at home. Her father said, "I feel so betrayed. I can't believe that Kayla would intentionally deceive us like that." Her mother said, "I trusted her. She's never lied to us like this before. I feel I can't ever trust her again."

The therapist again worked to help the parents understand that an eating disorder will lead a young person to feel so desperate that they will engage in behaviors that are quite out of character for them. "The fact that Kayla deceived you doesn't mean she is bad or manipulative," she said.

> It means she is feeling under such pressure from the eating disorder that she will do almost anything it is telling her to do. Her behavior doesn't show us she is a bad person. It shows us she is not able to cope with the pressure the eating disorder is putting on her. It shows us she is unable to make good decisions right now. It shows us how much she needs your help.

The therapist encouraged the parents to reflect on how the AN had changed Kayla and emphasized that AN affects almost all young people in this way. She helped them see that Kayla herself would not deceive her parents, that she did something out of character because the eating disorder was making decisions for her. The therapist then urged the family to redouble their efforts to free Kayla from the AN so as to protect her from further harm.

Over time, Jack and Caroline got better and better at distinguishing between things Kayla would say and do normally versus things she would say and do when "driving under the influence of AN." Kayla's siblings also became more understanding. Whereas previously they had withdrawn in anger when Kayla's AN behaviors were strong, they now did a wonderful job of ignoring AN behaviors when they occurred but then quickly stepping in afterwards to engage with Kayla in positive ways. Kayla was able to make good use of the distractions her siblings provided for her when she was agitated before or after mealtimes. The positive relationship with her siblings was a critically important factor in protecting Kayla's fragile self-esteem. Jack and Caroline also found ways to stay close to Kayla even when there was significant conflict in their relationship when they had to push back hard against what the AN wanted.

How Struggling to Externalize BN Affected FBT

Grace and her family had been attending FBT for BN for about six weeks and things were in a better place than they had been at the very beginning. Grace had been eating more regularly, her weight had stabilized, and her binge and purge episodes had decreased. Then they had a break from therapy for a couple of weeks over the winter holidays. When they came to the next session in January, Grace's parents were very upset. Her mother, Katherine, said, "We've had the worst Christmas you can imagine. Things have been horrible. Grace has been binge eating and vomiting constantly. It's worse than ever. Grace has put us all through so much. We can't take it anymore!" Her sister, Julie, described how one night she had friends over and she found a cup filled with vomit under the couch. She barely managed to conceal it from her friends. She was furious with Grace. "It's just not fair," Julie said. "I can't have any kind of normal life. Grace ruins everything!" Grace's father, Martin, said,

> This is putting too much of a strain on everyone. It's not fair to Julie. She has rights too. She should be able to have friends over without having to deal with something like that. There is no excuse for Grace's actions. She knows perfectly well that this is completely unacceptable behavior. It's not like we haven't told her this before. It has to stop.

The therapist asked Grace if she wanted to make a change, and if so, what would the change be? Grace said she wanted the episodes of binge eating and purging to stop.

The therapist then asked Grace to describe how she felt after the binge-purge episodes. "From talking to a lot of people with BN," the therapist said,

> I know that most people feel really guilty the next day if they have had a binge the previous night, so they feel they really, really need to restrict today in order to try to make up for all the food they had last night. Is that feeling familiar to you?

Grace said that she was desperately feeling she needed to restrict because of the binge episodes. However, Grace did not see a connection between the fact she had restricted during the day and the fact that her urge to binge and purge was then stronger than usual at night. She was entirely preoccupied with the drive to restrict.

The therapist then asked the parents whether, given what Grace was saying, they felt that Grace was ready to make the "right" choices. Both Martin and Katherine agreed it seemed she was not. The therapist emphasized that the eating disorder was still very much affecting Grace's ability to see clearly and the eating disorder was driving Grace to engage in ED behaviors that were dangerous and destructive. She reminded the parents that Grace needed them to protect her from the influence of BN, as she was unable to protect herself.

The therapist then talked with the family about how the BN was affecting Grace emotionally. Both parents said they could see that Grace was embarrassed about the binge and purge behaviors. The therapist asked them how they thought Grace felt earlier in the session when her sister Julie had described finding the mug filled with vomit under the couch. Both Martin and Katherine said they thought Grace probably felt ashamed. The therapist checked with Grace to see if this was correct. Grace started to cry. The therapist asked Julie what it was like for her to both feel upset about what had happened when her friends were over and also to see her sister suffering today. Julie also started to cry, and said, "I was just upset. I wasn't trying to make Grace feel bad."

Martin and Katherine were able to comfort both of their daughters and to begin to reframe what had happened. Katherine said, "You know, Julie, it's OK that you were upset. That's normal, given what happened. So, you don't have to feel badly about being upset. But we also don't want Grace to feel badly, because this is not her fault either." And then Martin stepped in to say,

> We just took our eye off the ball. Looking at it now, I can see we just weren't giving Grace the amount of support she needed. It's not her fault. It's not anyone's fault. Grace has an illness and we are all here to help her though it. We are going to make this better.

When the family were better able to understand that BN was strongly influencing what Grace was thinking and feeling and how this was driving her behaviors, they understood that she needed more support. They also understood that when they responded to Grace's challenging BN behaviors with frustration, this only made Grace feel worse about herself and did not help her learn to do things differently. In separating Grace from her BN behaviors, the family could see what they needed to do to help her, and they were also able to take a step closer to each other to help everyone in the family feel they were going to support each other and get though a tough situation together.

The Challenge of Externalizing ARFID in FBT

> Jimmy's parents, Linda and Timothy, had struggled to feed him almost since the day he was born. He arrived before time, almost six weeks preterm, and spent three weeks in the NICU before they could take him home. He didn't latch on well to breastfeed, and so Linda switched to bottle feeding him very early on. He took breast milk in the bottle but would refuse formula, crying and turning his head away as soon as he tasted it. He wasn't a hungry baby. He would fall asleep before the bottle was finished and they would wonder whether they should wake him up to get him to feed more, or whether they should let him sleep. When Linda and Timothy introduced solid foods, Jimmy often spat them out in disgust. He would eat only a very limited range of foods, mostly "white" foods, like bread, garlic bread, chicken nuggets, yogurt (only peach flavor, only one specific brand), Cheerios, Goldfish crackers, and lots of candy. As Jimmy got older, Linda and Timothy tried to get him to eat other foods, but he would dissolve into anxious tantrums, even if the "new" food was very similar to something he was already eating. Their pediatrician

recommended Jimmy be assessed by an eating disorder professional, who then diagnosed Jimmy with ARFID. Jimmy was 7 years old and likely had had ARFID all his life, but this was the first Linda and Timothy had heard of this disorder.

In their FBT sessions for ARFID, Linda and Timothy described their long struggle to feed Jimmy. They described his lack of interest in food, his pickiness, and his anxious tantrums when new foods were introduced. They also identified that one of the things that made it difficult to feed Jimmy was that he didn't stay still at the table long enough to eat. He would say he was full and would leave the table. Linda described how she felt she was constantly chasing after Jimmy with food. Linda and Timothy were exhausted and also exasperated. Timothy said,

> I'm sure Jimmy actually would like cheese pizza if he tried it. It's so similar to the garlic bread that he already eats. And it would make life easy if he would just eat a piece of plain pizza when we have it delivered. I'm so frustrated that he won't even try it. He's just being stubborn.

Linda said, "He just won't cooperate, not even a small bit. He's getting too old to behave this way."

The therapist worked to help Linda and Timothy understand more about ARFID and how children with ARFID tend to behave around food. She tried to help Linda and Timothy to see how ARFID was impacting on Jimmy's behavior. Both Linda and Timothy found it difficult to separate Jimmy from the food-related behaviors, partly because the eating behaviors had been a struggle for so long. The diagnosis was new, but the behaviors were not, and so it was a challenge for Linda and Timothy to completely change the way they were thinking about Jimmy's behaviors.

Linda and Timothy also struggled to see how they might help Jimmy eat more. They tended to think that the change would have to come from Jimmy. For example, when the therapist asked about what Jimmy had been eating, Linda said,

> But that's what I've been trying to tell you, he doesn't eat. I keep telling him he needs to eat more. I give him the food. But he won't eat it, no

matter what I tell him. He knows the consequences. If he's not going to eat, he's not going to grow. He says he wants to grow. He says he hates being the smallest in his class. Well, I told him, if you want to grow you have to eat your food. But he won't do it. I don't know what else to do.

Over time, the therapist helped Linda and Timothy understand more about how ARFID was impacting on Jimmy's awareness of hunger cues, his sense of feeling "full" after eating just a small amount of food, and his extreme sensitivity to food smells, tastes, and textures. As they began to better understand what Jimmy was experiencing, Linda and Timothy were able to support him to tolerate the changes that needed to happen for him to gain weight and grow. Whereas they had been thinking Jimmy was "difficult" they now saw him as a child who was experiencing sensory sensitivities that could cause anyone to struggle to eat enough. Their increased ability to understand that Jimmy had an illness that was driving his behaviors helped Linda and Timothy support Jimmy in a way that was empathic and also helped them more successfully intervene to bring about improved nutrition and weight gain.

In these examples, the parents struggled to understand that their child had an illness which was causing them to think and feel in a certain way, and that these experiences were driving the child's behavior. Parents tend to think that their child can make a free choice to change their behavior. Since the eating disorder behaviors are both challenging and destructive, parents expect their child to obey when they tell him to stop. When that doesn't happen, parents can become frustrated with their child. This frustration is unlikely to help the child to make changes and may make it even harder for the child to change, as the worse he feels about himself the more vulnerable he usually is to the demands of the eating disorder. When parents begin to see the ways in which the eating disorder has taken over their child's thinking and behavior, and to understand the kind of help their child actually needs, parents can be more successful in helping their child overcome the eating disorder.

Figure 6.1 Do not try to reason with an eating disorder: Why trying to reason with a child with eating-disordered thinking doesn't work
Nandini Datta

6
Do Not Try to Reason With an Eating Disorder: Why trying to reason with a child with eating-disordered thinking doesn't work

> She's so smart and always has been. She just needs a better explanation about why she needs to stop all this. She's always been so logical and rational! Why can't we just have a conversation about this?
>
> Mother of a 14-year-old girl with Anorexia Nervosa

Parents often remember their child before they had an eating disorder as a reasonable, logical, rational person (as much as any young person can be). Thus, it is a common area of distress and frustration around how having an eating disorder appears to "hijack" the young person, making them an irrational, illogical, tantrum-throwing stranger. The good news is—this is not the child's usual way of thinking. This change in their thinking has happened as a result of developing an eating disorder.

DOI: 10.4324/9781003353041-7

One of the things parents often hope to try to do is get their child to understand the logic and importance of eating to treat this debilitating illness. This may result in a lot of circular arguments with the young person about what they should or shouldn't be eating, arguments that go something like this:

Child: I'm not eating that, no way.

Parent: You have to—haven't you heard what the doctors have said? You're losing weight! Eating this/eating consistently/trying this is what will help you get better.

Child: That's disgusting. That's not even healthy, I'm not eating that. Plus, I am not even hungry right now.

Parent: But you need to eat, surely you can understand what the doctors are saying!

Child: Yeah, but they didn't say to eat that specifically. I've never eaten that and I'm not starting now.

We call this getting into debates with the eating disorder. Parents may have found that they are not very effective at getting their point across, or that these kinds of arguments are not very useful. Sometimes, these arguments may even interfere with the original goal parents had in mind—helping their child eat a healthier meal or snack—by spending time arguing instead of eating. One way to think about the reason these types of conversations aren't effective is to realize that they suggest the young person's understanding of healthy eating logically is the problem. But many people with eating disorders, particularly AN or BN, may have a lot of knowledge of dietary health and nutrition—counting calories and keeping meticulous watch on nutrition labels—none of which leads to making healthy choices or adopting a healthy diet. In fact, this information is often selectively processed in service of maintaining the eating disorder.

For those with ARFID, these types of conversations often go the same way, but sometimes for different reasons—here, the disgust or anxiety around trying new foods overrides any logic that is necessary to partake in a conversation about health. Also, age may play a factor as younger kids with ARFID are usually less able to engage in a rational discussion because their reasoning abilities are still developing. As many parents have noted, these types of conversations may end up being more maddening than useful, as a young person with an eating disorder is unable to grasp the "why" they need to eat. In sum, eating-disordered thinking is not rational or logical, and it gives the child (and parents) a hard time when reasoned with.

Trying to dissuade a young person with an eating disorder from engaging in their current eating behaviors or compensatory behaviors is just not effective and may result in more strife and tears than if parents didn't try to reason with their child. Another downside parents may notice is feeling completely depleted after these fruitless fights. This is not helpful because parents need their energy to be firm and maintain boundaries around mealtimes. Indeed, one of the most important strategies during the recovery process is limiting emotional outbursts around meals, which means fewer circular arguments with the eating disorder. We have heard from parents in the past that not getting pulled into debating what and how much to eat helps get through meals more quickly and with less conflict. How? Luckily, there are several things that can be done to help mealtimes go more smoothly.

This strategy may initially sound more relevant with a misbehaving toddler than with the young person with the eating disorder, but it is very important: *selective ignoring*. We use the phrase "don't negotiate with terrorists" in FBT. This might sound dramatic, but what it means is that eating-disordered thinking is the irrational terrorist (who has hijacked the healthy version of the child) and this has lead the young person to use all sorts of wily pseudo-arguments and senseless reasons not to finish a meal or snack. But it is important to remember that this is eating-disordered thinking, and if parents refuse to engage or negotiate with these irrational demands, it will be in the best interest of the overall health of their child. Usually, in these instances, engaging with irrational eating disorder statements results in meal-distracting behavior, leaving all involved upset and emotionally depleted. Instead, selectively ignoring or not paying attention to eating disorder-fueled conversations will preserve necessary energy and allow the meal to proceed with fewer negotiations or arguments. This is not to say that the meal will look the way meals used to before the eating disorder, but it will eliminate one conflict-filled aspect of the process. Eating disorder-fueled behaviors may include arguments as discussed, but they may also include other behaviors such as taking longer to finish a meal, cutting food into smaller pieces, picking apart certain foods, crying, or pleading with one parent. These too are often best responded to by not trying to argue but instead by simply stating that the meal—whether in pieces or not—needs to be finished, no debating. On the other hand, if the young person *is* engaging in a healthy way around some aspect of food or eating, that absolutely deserves praise and attention.

Some eating disorders—particularly AN—unlike other mental health disorders such as depression or anxiety disorders, are considered *egosyntonic*. That means that they may feel protective or good for the person with an eating disorder. In other words, the young person may be acting in ways to protect their eating disorder rather than eliminate it. Similar to anxiety, these behaviors fuel the eating disorder and strengthen the symptoms often seen (avoiding certain foods due to fear or disgust, restrictive eating, various compensatory behaviors). From a parent or outsider's vantage point, the eating disorder is disrupting the young person's developmental process, but from the young person's viewpoint, what they are doing may make complete sense to them. This means it is even more difficult to have rational conversations about needing to eat meals and snacks that support recovery, because while it makes sense to parents and the child's treatment team, it sounds terrifying and daunting to the young person with an eating disorder. In these moments, what is the most helpful for the young person to focus on is the act of getting through each meal and snack, rather than discussing *what* they will be eating, *when* they will be eating, *how much* they will be eating, or *why* they need to eat. When a young person's eating-related worries and fears interfere with reasonable eating, these decisions need to be made for them by parent(s)—meaning there are fewer things for the young person with the eating disorder to worry about. Now, their focus can be on the most daunting task at this point in recovery and treatment—making it through the meal. And if that can be achieved with minimal attention paid to eating disorder negotiations and arguments, the young person learns that antics and avoidance strategies that their eating disorder encourages them to use are just not sustainable. Selective ignoring means these types of arguments and behaviors are not being reinforced and are no longer effective in throwing a meal or snack off course.

FBT works to help instill two important ideas in parents and the young person with the eating disorder. One—that the eating disorder is an illness disrupting the child's developmental process and is separate from who the child is and was before they developed an eating disorder (See Chapter 5). Remembering this may help remind parents and, importantly, the young person that eating-disordered thinking is an irrational, illogical disorder, and *not* who they are as a person. And two—it is important to remember that FBT focuses on stopping all disordered-eating-related behaviors. The treatment and therapist will support and empower parental efforts to take action against dangerous restrictive or selective eating, over-exercising, binge eating, purging, or any other behaviors that are maintaining the eating disorder. This work is difficult but is distinct from engaging in debates lead by eating-disordered thinking. Instead, trying to rationalize with the disorder can interfere with FBT and the progress parents and families may otherwise be making.

In each of the vignettes below, we illustrate how parents learn that eating-disordered "thinking" is not rational thinking at all, but rather fear- and anxiety-based worry disguised as reasonable arguments. The vignettes illustrate examples of parents learning that negotiating with the disorder interferes with FBT progress and is frustrating for them and their child.

How Trying to Reason With Anorexia Nervosa Interferes With Progress in FBT

Kiran was 14 when she was diagnosed with AN. She was the child of two professional parents (one doctor and one engineer) who always appreciated their straight-A, hard-working, and rule-abiding daughter. In addition to being an exemplar student in several honors-level courses, Kiran was a dedicated Bharatanatyam (a classical Indian dance) dancer. When she went in for her yearly physical, Kiran's parents were surprised and dismayed to learn that Kiran was severely underweight, had stopped having her period due to malnutrition, and was almost at the point of needing hospitalization to improve her vital signs. The physician emphasized the importance for Kiran of having three meals and three snacks daily to improve her weight, and encouraged her parents to look for a therapist who may be able to help treat Kiran's AN. Kiran's parents first thought they would be able to correct these behaviors on their own. Their daughter was, after all, a smart, well-behaved kid. Not like some of her trouble-making peers. They were reluctant to admit that their daughter had an eating disorder and that they may need some professional support. Kiran's parents quickly learned over the next few days that something was different with Kiran. Trying to reason with her and explain from a logical, medical, or physiological and nutritive perspective that she needed to eat more consistently if she wanted to continue dancing was simply not working. If anything, it was making her angrier, and interfering with meals and snacks! Kiran continued to lose weight and seemed completely oblivious to the dangers this was putting her health under. In fact, some of the arguments seemed to take the entire duration of the meal, leaving Kiran in tears, her parents completely frustrated, and the meal untouched. Kiran's parents were shocked to learn of other behaviors their daughter was engaging in that seemed completely unlike her—hiding food in her sleeves during dinner, having outbursts before mealtimes when she saw what was being prepared, and talking back to parents disrespectfully. Kiran's parents talked amongst themselves and realized they needed some support around this. They found an FBT therapist and set up an appointment, feeling overwhelmed and out of their depth, but mostly, terrified for their daughter.

Kiran's parents' attempts to rationalize with the healthy part of their daughter are not uncommon for parents who are dealing with AN. But it is not an effective strategy, as they ultimately realized. Kiran's parents remembered the vivacious, studious child Kiran used to be—and this departure from that image of their daughter was hard for them to reconcile with how she was after she became ill with AN. But the energy and time spent trying to reason with Kiran (only to be met by the hardheaded eating disorder) was working against them—especially when these arguments occurred during mealtimes. Her parents and Kiran left meals largely uneaten, feeling depleted. In these instances, the AN "irrationality" had triumphed. And worse, Kiran had learned that engaging in "anorexic arguments" or throwing tantrums around meals could be an effective strategy to avoid eating. Her parents were correct to seek support from an expert at this time, who would help provide psycho-education around anorexic arguments and how to avoid them.

Kiran's parents shifted uncomfortably in their chairs and glanced at their mutinous, half-slumped daughter who was bouncing her leg up and down furiously, refusing to make eye contact with anyone in the room. The therapist before them had introduced the premise of FBT and charged the parents with managing meals and snacks in this first phase of treatment. Kiran's parents hesitatingly shared that they had been trying to increase meals as the pediatrician had recommended, but that this hadn't worked. They also shared that they had offered various incentives for eating, but this also did not seem to appeal to Kiran anymore. Instead, these attempts seemed to have resulted in countless arguments, and other behaviors such as hiding food to get through a meal. Kiran rolled her eyes at this and refused to answer any questions posed by the therapist, slumping down further in her chair. While her parents were mortified at Kiran's behavior, the therapist did not seem surprised. Instead, the therapist calmly explained that the appeals parents were making to their daughter to listen to reason and logic were being combatted by AN—not uncommon for this illness, given its egosyntonic nature. Kiran's parents hadn't heard of this word, and were somewhat relieved to learn that the tantrums, hiding food, and irrational behavior were due to the disorder their child had. Hearing this made Kiran's parents feel more resolved than ever to get their daughter back on track, and they were eager to hear how they might do this from their FBT therapist.

In this first session of FBT, her parents learned about the egosyntonic nature of AN, and how this makes appealing to the rational side of their daughter near to impossible. Instead, the therapist suggested the parents consider firmness and creating non-negotiable boundaries around mealtimes to help avoid such arguments. For instance, her parents could come up with a "mantra" to repeat during mealtimes when their daughter tried to engage them in an argument or nego-tiation about how much to eat. An example of a mantra could be, "We know this is difficult, but we are here for you," coupled with firm resolve around how much they expected Kiran to eat. Kiran's parents learned how and when to implement this mantra in their second session of FBT, where the therapist observed a family meal and gave *in vivo* feedback. She pointed out times that one or both parents began to argue or reason with Anorexia, highlighting how fruitless the argument was. The parents left the session feeling tired but empowered and with a better understanding of what to do during difficult mealtimes.

Over the course of the treatment, Kiran's parents learned to appreciate that trying to reason with AN was not helpful. They even began to recognize glimpses of the "old" Kiran emerging as treatment went on. During these instances, when they recognized Kiran making healthy choices, they praised and engaged with her to give positive feedback and promote her recovery. They found FBT helpful in learning what to reserve their energy for—so it did not get depleted in useless arguments with the eating disorder. And, hap-pily, they noticed these type of arguments became less and less frequent as Kiran moved through treatment.

How Trying to Reason with Bulimia Nervosa and Binge Eating Interferes With Progress

Taylor had always been a bubbly, outgoing girl. She made the competitive gymnastics team in her sophomore year of high school, after which her parents noticed some changes in her behavior. Taylor began to come home from school absolutely ravenous and take large amounts of food up to her room. This typically was snack-type foods, like family-sized bags of chips, leftover Halloween candy, and Hostess cakes. Taylor's mom gently asked if she had been eating okay at school, noticing that Taylor's lunch often came back untouched and that she had been taking just an apple or piece of fruit in the morning. Taylor brushed it off saying she ate fine. Along with this behavior Taylor began spending longer periods of time in the bathroom, particularly in the evening after dinner. Taylor's parents brought up their concerns with Taylor's pediatrician, who recommended they seek a formal eating disorder assessment. Taylor met with a clinical psychologist and, after establishing a good rapport, Taylor admitted that she had been engaging in daily binge and purge episodes to control her weight, and that this cycle had been becoming increasingly out of control over the past several weeks. She reported feeling pressure from her gymnastics team to be a certain weight and shape optimal for her sport. The clinician recommended FBT for BN to Taylor and her family, which Taylor was very resistant to. At the onset of treatment, Taylor's parents expressed to the clinician that they hoped the clinician could spend more time one-on-one with Taylor explaining the harmful effects of her behavior. They felt very strongly that if Taylor understood the logic behind why she should not engage in the harmful binge-purge cycle, she would be cured! After all, Taylor had behaved in risky ways before, and talking her through her choices had always been helpful.

Taylor's parents understandably felt pulled by the need to explain to their daughter that her behavior was harmful to her physical health and functioning. Why couldn't she just see how dangerous this behavior was to her heart, her electrolyte balance, her teeth, and her life? Taylor had a history of engagement in risky adolescent behavior, such as underage drinking and breaking curfew, and oftentimes these issues had resolved with good heart-to-hearts and boundaries placed. They wanted the FBT therapist to have a similar heart-to-heart with Taylor and help her understand how unreasonable and unhealthy her binge eating and purging behaviors were so she would be motivated to stop engaging in them.

Taylor's parents and Taylor struggled in the first few sessions of FBT, with Taylor's parents wanting to emphasize the harm Taylor was doing to her teeth and her physical health, and appealing to the rational side of their daughter. Taylor felt infuriated that her parents thought she could "turn off a switch" and stop her ED behaviors. This ensued in several rounds of finger pointing and arguments about how to best manage the symptoms. The therapist helped redirect the conversation to understand that the behaviors Taylor was engaging in needed to be disrupted, rather than arguing about the lack of logic or rationale behind the behaviors. The therapist reminded Taylor and her parents that the best outcomes of FBT are when these behaviors are interrupted early in treatment. Taylor's parents agreed to put the logic and rational conversation aside and get on the same page to help support their daughter with firm boundaries and strategies. Taylor herself seemed relieved at this shift in conversation.

Once Taylor's parents began to understand how to support Taylor in the context of her eating disorder and this treatment, Taylor felt more supported. This may be because her parents were now providing non-judgmental support, demonstrating empathy, and providing clear boundaries that helped support Taylor's navigation of overcoming binge eating and purging behaviors. In trying to appeal to Taylor's logic and reason, Taylor may have felt that her parents were implying that the eating disorder behaviors were volitional and a choice she was making, when she actually felt helpless and out of control. She may have felt as though her parents did not see how much she struggled daily with trying to do her best to eat consistently and feeling disheartened when unable to. FBT and the clinician guiding this treatment helped her parents and Taylor work initially on disrupting the behaviors in a consistent manner, rather than focusing on rationale and logic. Once Taylor and her parents got into the swing of treatment, they began to progress through treatment and eventually through Taylor's recovery more smoothly.

How Trying to Reason With Avoidant/Restrictive Food Intake Disorder (ARFID) Interferes With FBT for ARFID

Juan was a young boy who was diagnosed with ARFID at age 10. He had always had a low appetite and hunger drive since he was an infant. As he got into his toddler years, Juan began to develop strong preferences for specific types of food. For example, Juan enjoyed a specific brand of cereal and was incredibly aware if this cereal was a different brand and refused to eat it. These preferences became increasingly stringent as Juan grew older, generalizing to types of chicken nuggets, pasta, and cheese crackers. His parents felt at a loss for what to do. Now, at age 10, Juan had a short list of six foods he ate from—specific cheese crackers, bow tie pasta, a particular brand of chicken nuggets, one type of cereal, one type of plan waffle, and vanilla ice cream. These limited choices interfered with Juan's school lunches, his ability to go to sleepovers, and other social events such as birthday parties, where his food preferences weren't taken into consideration. Juan's pediatrician pointed out that as Juan approached adolescence, he was not making sufficient progress on his growth chart. The pediatrician encouraged his parents to seek therapy to help address Juan's eating habits in addition to taking nutritional supplements and vitamins. Juan's parents agreed to try FBT for ARFID, seeking the consultation of an expert. Juan's mom expressed that she felt sick of being a short order cook at each meal, and both of Juan's parents felt generally exhausted after meals.

As is sometimes the case with ARFID, which has often been a problem for many years before starting treatment, Juan's parents had tried to help him eat any way they could which often meant accommodating Juan's highly restrictive eating patterns because of his ARFID. In an effort to try to both meet his nutritional needs and help reduce the effort each meal took, they had become "short order cooks" and learned to dread mealtimes, which were often fraught with conflict.

At the close of the first session, Juan's parents were tasked with creating an "always, sometimes, never" list where they were asked to list foods that Juan always ate, could eat with some difficulty ("sometimes" foods) and foods that would be very challenging for Juan, but helpful if he were able to eat (for example, quesadilla with chicken, a dish Juan's mom frequently made for the family). In session 2, they brought a meal to the session that included items from these categories—including a quesadilla. When trying to get Juan to have a bite, his parents tried reasoning with him about the importance of having a variety of foods and reminded him of what his pediatrician said regarding his weight and vitamin imbalance. Juan's father pointed out that Juan enjoyed the flavor of cheese, and that this food was filled with delicious cheese! Throughout this, Juan got more and more grumpy, eventually shoving his plate away and plopping his face down on the table and refusing to look up. Juan's parents explained that in other areas of his life, Juan was such a reasonable child, they could not understand his difficulty here. The therapist used this as an opportunity to "externalize" ARFID, pointing out to Juan's parents that his posture and behavior may be indicative of his parents effectively challenging the illness, rather than Juan being irrational and rude. The therapist also highlighted that Juan was still a reasonable child, and that this behavior was more likely the ARFID being challenged in the context of a new food.

Juan's parents were learning that Juan's behaviors and eating disorder could not be reasoned with or be faced with logic; rather, there were some behavioral strategies that might be more effective in getting Juan to try a bite of quesadilla (a behavioral goal Juan's parents had agreed would constitute as meaningful progress towards challenging ARFID). The therapist helped the parents explore other strategies during this family meal session, including being clear about the behavior they wanted to change, continuing to use language to externalize the ARFID rather than trying to reason with it or blame Juan, and asking the parents to decide whether or not an incentive would be helpful. Juan's parents decided together that if Juan tried a bite of his quesadilla, he would be allowed to have 20 extra minutes playing a favorite game of his. Calm, repetitive reminders of this, along with behavioral strategies such as moving the plate closer to Juan and remaining firm in their resolve, helped support Juan and, eventually, he managed to take one bite. The therapist used this opportunity to praise Juan's parents for their effective behavior, highlighting what *does* work in challenging ARFID versus what may not be as fruitful (i.e., having a conversation with ARFID).

The therapist worked with the family to ensure that new foods were being incorporated into his meals routinely. The concept of gradually branching out by trying foods that were similar to Juan's "always" foods was helpful and reminded his parents that as tempting as it might be, efforts to explain or rationalize why a food was important or similar would not be useful or effective. Juan's parents ultimately saw the importance of this while also recognizing that the bulk of arguments around meals were against ARFID fears and worries rather than blaming Juan.

Over the course of FBT for ARFID, Juan and his family worked together to move forward in ways to increase Juan's eating from a non-judgmental and supportive standpoint. This is not to say the journey wasn't met with some ups and downs, but helping eliminate the arguments wherein his parents tried to reason with ARFID helped both Juan and his parents move towards his eating goals.

These cases demonstrate the importance of not buying into eating disorder-driven irrational arguments and delaying tactics, as the purpose of this is to try to keep the young person from making changes in their eating-disordered behaviors. Regardless of the type of eating disorder, it is important for parents to learn to sidestep these types of negotiations and remind themselves that eating disorders have caused their child to be temporarily irrational or confused and a poor decision maker about eating and nutrition. The earlier parents appreciate the importance of not expecting their child to be reasonable when they have an eating disorder, the easier it will be on the entire family to combat the behaviors that maintain the eating disorder.

Figure 7.1 Deferring to experts is not the answer: How expecting other professionals to solve the problem can interfere with progress in FBT
Nandini Datta

7
Deferring to Experts Is Not the Answer: How expecting other professionals to solve the problem can interfere with progress in FBT

> We need more help. FBT is not enough!
>> Parent of a young person with an eating disorder

Families Can Get Off-Track During FBT Because They Believe the Solution Lies in an Outside Factor

Many parents struggle to take effective action to address their child's ED because they believe that the solution to the problem lies in something other than their own actions in combating these behaviors. Often parents get stuck in feelings of frustration because they believe that the FBT therapist should be giving them more clear directions about what they should do, or exactly

DOI: 10.4324/9781003353041-8

how they should do it. Many parents get stalled because they believe that their child should be getting individual therapy instead of, or in addition to, FBT. And some parents experience confusion around whether their child's symptoms are a result of a medical problem rather than an eating disorder. The danger with each of these situations lies in the fact that while parents are waiting and hoping for an outside factor to change, they tend to hold back from putting *all* of their energy into the one thing that is most likely to be effective: their efforts at every opportunity, every day, to intervene to stop ED behaviors like restriction, binge eating, purging and over-exercise. This chapter focuses on how parents can avoid the situation where they inadvertently get off track in their efforts to intervene against ED symptoms due to a belief that their child needs a different kind of help other than that which they themselves are providing.

> We don't know what to do and the FBT therapist doesn't tell us. She is the expert. We need her to tell us exactly what to do. Why can't she just give us a list of instructions so that we can follow them?

Anyone who has been through the experience of working to help their child recover from an eating disorder will attest to the fact that it is an extraordinarily challenging experience. And so, it seems natural that parents expect professionals to give them clear instructions on what they need to do to help their child. After all, that is what would happen if their child had been diagnosed with a different serious illness: the medical team would explain exactly what the treatment plan was going to be, with a calendar for when the interventions would happen. The medical team would be *responsible* for the interventions, and the patient and parents would be supported through the process.

How different this is from the experience of parents of young people with eating disorders, where the FBT therapist tells them that *they* must be the ones who intervene to support their child to recover. And not only must they be the ones who do it, they must also figure out *how* to do it in their family context. The therapist says that she will help them, but that she can't give them specific instructions on exactly how it is done. And this can feel incredibly frustrating for parents who are desperately worried about their child. Here is a quote from a mother:

> I don't know what to do. You're the therapist. You are an expert in eating disorders. I ask you every week what I should do, and you keep telling me the same thing, that I need to figure it out myself. But I don't know what to do, that's why I'm here! I need you to help me!

When a parent says something like this, FBT therapists can find themselves wishing that there were, in fact, a set of clear step-by-step instructions that they could provide to parents. But the truth is, just as there is no one *right* way to raise a child, there is also no one right way to manage ED behaviors. Parents of young people with very similar ED symptoms make very different choices around *how* to address those symptoms, and yet they can each be successful in their own strategies. One way to think of this is that while AN is quite uniform, families and parents are different and the result is that what works for one family may not work for another and, importantly, there is more than one way to do it well.

The FBT therapist can't know for sure what will be the best strategy for the family in front of her, but she is there to help the parents figure out what strategy they think will work *right now*. And in each session the therapist will help the parents look at how things went in the past week, help them reflect on whether what they are doing is working, and support them to decide if they want to keep doing the same thing or make some changes.

This is difficult for parents, because the process of finding their way is almost always fraught with anxiety, setbacks, and *a lot* of conflict, not least because if the parents' strategy is successful then their child's distress often initially *increases*, leading to more struggle. But the therapist will work to help parents describe what they were thinking and feeling that led them to choose their course of action, and whether, talking together about it now, they want to keep to the same strategy, modify it, or scrap it and try something else entirely. The therapist will join with the parents in their efforts to come up with potential solutions that might work for them, but it is the parents who will decide on their strategies, and the therapist will respect their decisions and their personal values. This is the kind of working together that we aim for in FBT.

Here's an example of how thinking the therapist has the answers can impede parents' ability to intervene successfully in their child's Bulimia Nervosa.

Diane and Joseph, the parents of 14-year-old Ethan, a boy with BN, had been trying for several weeks to intervene in his pattern of restricting, bingeing and purging. After their first FBT session they began to sit with Ethan for each meal and snack, explaining to him that he must eat. Ethan became more and more upset. He shouted at his parents, and he threw food onto the floor. Sometimes, after Diane and Joseph had succeeded in getting him to eat, Ethan immediately ran to the bathroom and vomited up the food. In their FBT sessions, Diane and Joseph described what was happening, saying, "We tried telling him he must eat, but it doesn't work. It just makes things worse. We don't know what else we can do."

The therapist praised Diane and Joseph for taking steps to help their child. She worked to help them understand that most young people with Bulimia Nervosa become more distressed when parents first begin to take action, and, in order to help their child overcome BN, parents must be patient, persistent, and not be deterred by setbacks. She encouraged them to continue with their efforts despite the difficulties. But Diane and Joseph were upset about the times when binges or purges still happened, and they were very worried by how emotionally upset Ethan became. Over the weeks, as Ethan continued to be distressed, Diane and Joseph felt frustrated with the therapist and decided to tell her they needed her to give them more clear directions on what to do.

Rather than giving them specific instructions, their therapist asked them lots of detailed questions about what had been happening. Diane and Joseph described what they had been doing to intervene against Ethan's ED behaviors. For example, they had prepared appropriate meals, plated them, and sat down together with Ethan at the table. They had explained to Ethan that he needed to eat regularly. They had also explained that his purging behaviors were dangerous and needed to stop. But they were worried that he was so distressed about eating, and that binge and purge episodes were still happening.

The therapist noted that Diane and Joseph had had some success with their strategies. Ethan's eating pattern was much more consistent than before. She encouraged Diane and Joseph to consider how they might intervene to prevent Ethan's behaviors of binge eating and purging. They agreed together to establish a rule that Ethan could not go to the bathroom for one hour after meals, or if he did need to, his father would keep "a foot in the door" which would allow for some privacy but prevent vomiting. They also planned to stay in the same room with Ethan in the evenings, the time he was most likely to binge.

In talking with Diane and Joseph about their experiences, their therapist asked them what they expected progress would look like if she were able to tell them exactly how to help Ethan. Diane and Joseph both replied that they believed that if the therapist would only tell them what to do then that strategy would work *immediately* and would be effective *every time*. When Ethan's reaction to Diane and Joseph's strategies to combat the ED was to be become more distressed or oppositional, they tended to conclude they must be "doing it wrong." Then, because they believed the therapist could tell them the "right" strategy to use, they held off from consistently using the strategies they had started with, even though they had in fact been making progress.

It took Diane and Joseph several more weeks to work this through in sessions, but they came to see that although BN behaviors were still happening, they were happening less frequently over time. As they began to focus more on consistently implementing their strategies, even if they didn't work perfectly every time, Diane and Joseph began to feel more confident. On one occasion, Diane said to the therapist, "I know you're probably going to say that it's up to us, but I wanted to ask you whether we should...." The therapist smiled and said that yes, she was going to say it was up to the parents. By this time, Diane and Joseph were not frustrated with the therapist's response. They understood that she was there to help them make decisions about interventions that felt right for them and their child. Ethan continued to make progress and they were able to move from phase 1 into phase 2 as he became better able to cope with eating regularly and avoiding engaging in binge and purge behaviors. Over the next several months, Ethan went on to make a good recovery.

Diane and Joseph had gotten stuck for some time because they believed that the therapist should be able to give them a strategy they could use that would "work" well every time. As they came to understood that there was no one right way to help their son, they felt more confident in their decisions, enough so that they could see them through consistently. They ultimately developed a number of strategies that over time worked for them and for Ethan.

Believing Your Child Has to "Buy In" to the Therapy In Order for It to Work

Our daughter was in individual therapy before we started FBT. She liked her therapist and she said she found the therapy helpful. But after several months we could see her ED was getting worse, not better. When we switched to FBT our daughter hated the sessions. She said that she felt that we weren't listening to her. She said that we only ever talked about how much she ate and that we didn't care about how she felt. She said she didn't like the therapist. She wanted us to stop FBT and let her do individual therapy again. We were tempted to agree, because what she was saying seemed to make sense. But we knew that she hadn't made any real progress in her individual therapy even though she felt it was supportive. We decided we would see FBT through to the end and then after that if our daughter still wanted individual therapy, she could do that then. With time, FBT did bring about a real change in our daughter's symptoms. And then, in the car on the way home from one of our sessions our daughter said, "You know, [the therapist] is actually really nice." We could hardly believe it. For months she had been saying she hated the therapist, but as she got better, she had a whole different attitude. And what's much more important, her ED was better.

It's not surprising that many parents believe their child *really* needs individual therapy for their eating disorder. After all, the popular understanding of how therapy works is that people talk to their therapist on a one-to-one confidential basis, and the goal of the therapy is for the person to gain insight into their problems. because once the person gains an understanding of *why* they feel as they do, it allows them to be able to make changes in their lives. Given this widespread cultural belief, it's natural that parents think that an individual therapeutic approach that aims to help the young person "see the light" would bring about the desired change in their child's thoughts, feelings, and behavior.

However, research shows us that this approach is generally not very effective in treating eating disorders in children and young people. Individual therapy for AN in teens, even when provided by expert eating disorder therapists, is less effective than FBT. Individual therapy takes much longer to get results, and the young person is more likely to need to be admitted to hospital during the course of individual treatment.

One of the main reasons individual therapy is less effective in eating disorders is that the young person typically does not see the eating disorder as a problem. At best, the young person will have limited motivation to change, and in fact, usually not only do they lack motivation to change, they have *huge* motivation to keep doing what they are doing, i.e., keep restricting, or over-exercising, or purging, and to keep doing this all the more every day. Even in cases where the young person does have some insight and motivation to change, it is not generally consistent enough to lead to behavior change on the scale that is needed. Unfortunately, even the very best eating disorder therapists cannot easily help the young person to turn the situation around.

There are many, many different forms of psychological talk therapies. Most are individual therapies, and some are in family, couples, or group format. But almost all psychological therapies rest on the premise that thoughts, feelings, and behaviors are linked, and that a change in any one of these will result in a change in the others. Some therapies focus more on changing thinking, some focus more on emotions, and some focus more on behaviors. The FBT approach focuses on supporting the parents to bring about behavior change first because with eating disorders it is the most successful strategy to achieve both physical *and* psychological recovery. This does not mean that FBT therapists are not interested in a young person's thoughts and feelings. They are very much concerned about the experience of the young person, but they focus on helping parents bring about behavior change first because with eating disorders, since the behaviors are dangerous, it is vital to intervene to protect the young person from further harm.

We do not recommend that the young person be in individual therapy for their eating disorder at the same time as being in FBT. It's not a good idea to be in two different therapies at once, as there is a danger of therapists working at cross purposes and giving different and therefore confusing messages to the young person and their family. Adding on individual therapy involves a risk of undermining the effectiveness of FBT, and there is, as yet, no evidence that the additional therapy improves outcomes. It may seems somewhat counter-intuitive, but more therapy is not usually better. Instead of having an additive effect, adding on a second therapy could dilute the effectiveness of the first therapy rather than doubling the strength of the treatment.

In cases where a young person is experiencing symptoms of another mental health problem, such as anxiety or depression or obsessive-compulsive disorder (OCD), parents may feel that their child needs some additional therapy to help them with that problem. We still recommend treating the eating disorder *first* because this is the priority, in much the same way that in an emergency medical situation we would first stop the bleeding and then look to see what else needs to be addressed. The interesting thing about co-occurring symptoms in eating disorders is that often when the eating disorder is successfully treated the other symptoms also improve. Sometimes though, the young person does indeed have another mental health problem in addition to the ED, and once FBT is finished it can then be helpful for the young person to engage in additional individual therapy to address their other difficulties. We need to pay attention to priorities and timing. We advise the FBT is done first to stabilize the eating disorder. First, we "stop the bleeding." Then we see what is left to do.

How Parents Believing Individual Therapy Is Needed Can Interfere With FBT

> We are trying to help Courtney, but she is fighting us every step of the way. She is not "buying in" to this FBT approach. She needs individual therapy to help her understand that she needs to change. We can support her, but she has to want it. It has to come from her.

In the quotation above, Courtney's mother Jeanna was trying to explain to their FBT therapist that she and her husband Tim were sure that their daughter needed individual therapy for AN. Mealtimes had become stressful, so much so that Jeanna and Tim were not just worried about Courtney's weight, they were worried about her mental state and were quite bewildered by the changes in her behavior. Up until the time Courtney developed AN at age 14, their style of interacting as a family had always been respectful and egalitarian. Jeanna and Tim strongly believed in the importance of listening to their children's wishes and taking their opinions into account in parenting decisions. Courtney had always been a cheerful, fair-minded, and considerate child who was close to her parents and her two sisters. Not only that, she was an excellent student, a talented artist, and a skilled athlete, who had always won the praise of her teachers and coaches. In all their years of parenting, Jeanna and Tim had never had a difficulty that they had struggled with for such a prolonged time. They couldn't understand why they were unable to work out this problem in their usual way, through talking together, listening to each other, and then agreeing on a decision on how to move forward.

Jeanna and Tim told their therapist they felt Courtney needed individual therapy to help her change what she was thinking and feeling, so that it would become easier for her to understand that she needed to eat more. The therapist explained that individual therapy takes longer to work than FBT and is generally less successful. He went on to ask them to describe how Courtney was reacting when they put food in front of her. Jeanna and Tim described Courtney's anxiety, agitation, and apparent inability to eat. The therapist asked them if, given the strength of the AN at that point in time, they thought that Courtney was strong enough to be able to fight the illness herself. On reflection, Jeanna and Tim both said that Courtney was not strong enough to fight the AN, but then Tim said this was why they thought she needed individual therapy, to help her reach a point where she wanted to recover. Both Jeanna and Tim said they were completely willing to help Courtney, but they felt it was wrong to "force" her to eat against her will, and they wanted her to have individual therapy as well as FBT. They were frustrated that their therapist said it had to be one or the other. They agreed, reluctantly, to continue with FBT.

However, the next day, Tim called the therapist to say that he and Jeanna were in the Emergency Department with Courtney because she had become very distressed after eating and she had then self-harmed by cutting. Jeanna and Tim felt this self-harm was a clear sign that Courtney needed individual therapy to help her manage her distress and to help change her ED cognitions so she could reach the point where she would want to recover.

Over the next several weeks, progress in FBT stalled. Jeanna and Tim were reluctant to "push" Courtney to eat, for fear she might self-harm. Courtney continued to restrict food intake, and her weight dropped even lower. Their therapist expressed his belief that what would help Courtney most was if her parents helped her to overcome her fears of eating and weight gain. He encouraged Tim and Jeanna to ensure that Courtney ate enough food to restore her to a healthy weight, and at the same time to stay close to her and do whatever they needed to do to keep her safe. The therapist urged the parents to remain calm and steer a steady course to recovery through consistent nourishment.

After several weeks of struggle, with very little progress, the therapist asked Tim and Jeanna to help him understand what it was that was getting in the way of their ability to successfully re-nourish their child. Jeanna and Tim both identified that they were waiting for Courtney to come around to understanding she needed to change. However, they saw that after many weeks Courtney did not seem to be gaining more insight. If anything, she seemed even more rigid and stuck than she had been before.

The therapist asked Jeanna and Tim what it was they thought would help their daughter at that moment in time. Both parents felt that Courtney needed to restore weight urgently, but they wanted it to happen in a way that caused her less distress. They wanted Courtney to choose to recover. Their therapist asked them if they felt Courtney was close to being able to do this, and both replied that they could see she was not, and their many attempts to reason with her had failed. They were perplexed by Courtney's impenetrability to reason. Their therapist then asked them what they would do if Courtney had a different life-threatening illness and was refusing treatment. Would they engage Courtney in individual therapy and wait for months hoping that she would "come to her senses" and agree to the treatment? Or would they take charge of the situation and ensure that their child had the treatment that would save her life, even if she didn't fully agree with their decision?

Jeanna and Tim decided that they did need to take charge and make the decision that was in the best interests of their child. They agreed they would push through the protest from the eating disorder. The therapist helped them come up with a plan for how they would keep Courtney safe even if she were very distressed. Jeanna and Tim planned that they would engage Courtney in individual therapy immediately after they were finished in FBT.

From that point onwards, progress in FBT was much better. Although Courtney initially was distressed, her parents remained calm and worked together to ensure that she was safe and also that she ate enough food to recover. Within a couple of months, Courtney's anxiety had eased considerably, and she was able to tolerate eating and weight gain. With her parents' support she continued to do well. The family progressed through stage 1 of FBT, then into stage 2 where Courtney began to take responsibility for independent eating, and finally into stage 3, where the family began to get more fully back to normal life. At the end of FBT, Courtney surprised her parents by saying that she didn't want individual therapy. She said that instead of attending therapy appointments she wanted to spend her time in school and sport activities and, more importantly, having fun with her friends.

Tim and Jeanna got off track for a period of time because they believed their child needed individual therapy to develop insight into her situation so that she would agree she needed to eat more in order to recover. Tim and Jeanna believed this insight should come first, and then Courtney would "work with" them and begin to make progress against her ED. However, Tim and Jeanna came to understand that it didn't make sense to waste time waiting and hoping that Courtney would change, when progress would happen more quickly if they stepped in to manage the situation until Courtney got to a stage where she was able to manage by herself. When the parents took charge and worked together to put all of their energy into re-nourishment efforts, Courtney began to make progress, so that ultimately she did recover, not only physically but also psychologically.

Sometimes parents feel that their child needs not just individual therapy, but a more intensive form of therapy such as residential or intensive day program treatment. It is important to be aware that there is little evidence that such treatments are effective in the long term and, what's more, they can sometimes make things worse rather than better. These programs often disrupt the young person's normal development by taking them out of their schooling and activities, and away from their friends and family. The young person may well make some progress while in the treatment, but relapse of the ED after discharge is common because what has been learned in these setting is hard to generalize to the real lives of adolescents. Disrupted school progress and disconnection with friends are serious barriers to a young person who is already struggling. Furthermore, as adolescence is the time when a young person is developing their sense of identity, there is the risk that such intensive treatment programs may solidify the young person's identity as a person with an eating disorder and often can lead them to develop social networks made up primarily of other young people with eating disorders, which in turn may actually make recovery more difficult. But what is perhaps most concerning is that relationships within a family are not strengthened by removing a child from their parents at a time when the child is suffering greatly. The benefit of FBT is that the young person learns to manage their eating disorder while at the same time managing the other challenges of ordinary life *while being supported by their family*. We believe this is why recovery in the context of FBT is more sustainable than recovery that happens in an artificial environment that comes at a very high cost to the young person's development and the family's relationships.

When Parents Worry Their Child Has an Untreated Medical Condition That Accounts for Some of Their Problem

Before treatment begins for any eating disorder, it is essential that the young person has had a comprehensive medical and psychological assessment. There are many potential medical explanations for eating disorder symptoms, and psychological conditions such as depression, anxiety, or OCD can also be associated with restriction of food intake, weight loss, vomiting, difficulty swallowing, or compulsive exercise. Prior to commencing FBT, it's necessary to clearly establish the ED diagnosis and rule out any other explanations for the symptoms.

However, there are times when parents worry that their child has a medical condition that was missed in their initial evaluation. And when this happens, it often leads parents to "push" less in their efforts to address eating-disordered behaviors. This is a somewhat tricky situation, as it is, of course, possible that the young person does have an underlying condition that is not yet diagnosed. In some situations, the medical doctors will be continuing to conduct investigations during the time that the family is in FBT therapy. However, the therapist may still work to help the family to "keep their eye on the ball" and work to combat the disordered eating symptoms. In general, even if there is a medical condition or an additional psychological disorder that is contributing to the young person's difficulties, they will still need to eat regularly, about three meals and two snacks per day. The challenge often arises when the young person resists eating, or vomits, and the parents are uncertain how they should respond because they feel uncertain whether the resistance is mostly psychological or is due to physical discomfort.

Although it can sometimes be difficult to know the answer to this question, the first thing to consider is that the truth may not be black or white, so that the "real" problem may not be either one thing or the other. For example, it may be that the young person is genuinely experiencing physical discomfort, but he also struggles with psychological fear of weight gain, or fear of choking, or fear of trying new foods. And it's important to remember that regardless of the origin of the difficulty, the young person still needs to eat enough food to be healthy, even if it means eating when not hungry, or eating when feeling uncomfortably full, or learning how to remain calm enough to keep from vomiting. FBT will aim to help parents ensure that their child is restored to a state of health, even though eating is difficult for them physically and/or psychologically.

To help parents identify which behaviors they want to target, the FBT therapist may ask the parents to observe how their child reacts to different foods, e.g., is the young person OK with eating steamed vegetables but not those same vegetables sautéed in breadcrumbs and butter? Will he drink lots of water but refuse to drink juice or milk? Are there foods the young person previously ate, such as pizza, ice cream, or birthday cake, that he now outright refuses? Will he eat foods like lettuce more easily? Or will he eat lots of ice cream and smoothies but refuse to eat crunchy foods? Answers to questions such as these may help parents to figure out whether their child's behaviors are mostly related to concerns about weight and shape, or fear of choking or sensory sensitivities, or problems like low appetite or nausea. And it will help parents decide where to focus their attention.

The therapist will also help parents take notice of the context and patterns of behavior like purging or eating very slowly. Do the behaviors occur consistently, or do they vary depending on a social context? If a young person is vomiting at home but not when friends are around, this suggests something other than a medical explanation for the behavior. And again, it's important to remember that even if a child has a medical condition that partly explains some of their symptoms, they will still have to change their behavior in order to be healthy, and it is still important for their parents to support them to do that.

How Parents Can Get Stuck in FBT Because of Worry About a Medical Problem Causing the Eating Disorders

Marco and Elaine were worried that their son Diego could have an undiagnosed medical problem that accounted for his difficulty swallowing food. Diego had always been an extremely "picky" eater, but he was not diagnosed with an eating disorder, ARFID, until he was 12 years old, when, after an episode where he briefly choked while eating meat, Diego began to eat less and less, saying he found it hard to swallow. The doctors had said there was no medical reason for the difficulty swallowing, but Diego insisted that he often couldn't get the food down. Meals could take hours, with Diego reluctantly putting food in his mouth, gagging, spitting out food, and swallowing with trepidation.

As all this had been happening for many months prior to starting FBT, Diego was significantly underweight. Marco and Elaine were not convinced that Diego's difficulty swallowing was solely due to psychological reasons such as an eating disorder or anxiety. They felt Diego could have a medical condition that had been missed in the evaluations and this condition was making it difficult for Diego to swallow. As a result of their concern, they held back from working assertively on increasing Diego's intake of food, and their progress in the initial weeks of FBT was very slow.

The FBT therapist encouraged Marco and Elaine to talk with their doctors again about their concerns. Then she worked to help them identify a strategy for how they would ensure that Diego ate enough food to restore weight. She helped them to think about whether there was some "middle path" they could take to help Diego eat more, regardless of whether the reason for his difficulty eating was medical, psychological, or a combination of both. The therapist asked them if there were some foods that Diego found easier to eat than others. They were able to identify that Diego did eat softer foods more easily. They described that he ate ice cream and drank smoothies without much difficulty. The therapist encouraged them to take a pragmatic approach and to start with "what works" and build on that. She helped Marco and Elaine see that they had been stuck on an idea that Diego needed to eat the types of food he had eaten before, and since he was now resistant to most of these, they had not had much success in increasing his intake. When Diego refused foods, insisting he could not swallow, Marco and Elaine tended to become upset and think that there must be a medical solution to the problem with swallowing. However, the therapist helped them understand that regardless of whether there was a medical issue, Diego still needed to take in enough nourishment to be healthy. Marco and Elaine began to see that it would be better if Diego had several smoothies or portions of ice cream per day rather than eating nothing at all. They agreed together to ask the doctors to re-assess whether there was anything that could have been missed in the initial medical evaluations, and at the same time to begin to increase Diego's intake of food by doing more of what was already working, with a plan to later re-introduce foods that Diego found more difficult to swallow.

The therapist also worked to help Marco and Elaine observe Diego's reactions to different types of foods. They observed that Diego could eat cookies without difficulty, even though these had to be chewed, whereas he was very resistant to eating bread, which had a similar texture. They noticed that he ate candy, chips, and chocolate much more easily than he would eat family meals, so that his difficulty swallowing was not consistent across preferred vs. non-preferred foods. Observing Diego's different reactions to swallowing foods of different taste but similar textures helped Marco and Elaine think about whether Diego's difficulty swallowing likely had a psychological component.

The therapist also worked to help Marco and Elaine observe Diego's eating behaviors in different contexts. Because Diego was not eating much during the school day, Marco and Elaine decided that one of them would go to the school each day and take Diego out to eat lunch in the car. They noticed that Diego ate much more quickly at these times, when he was motivated to finish the task of eating lunch so that he could go play with his friends in the schoolyard.

In talking through these observations in session, the parents were able to consider that if Diego could eat at a better pace in some situations, then it was reasonable to think he could learn to eat at a better pace at home also. They began to work much more confidently and consistently on reducing the time it took for Diego to complete meals and snacks, and they began to have more success with helping him eat a wider range of foods. Once Marco and Elaine moved beyond their "stuck point," Diego began to make weight improvements each week. Their FBT therapist helped them become good "anthropologists" who observed their child's behavior in a non-judgmental way. They learned to remove the emotion from their observations and to focus in a pragmatic way on deciding together how to intervene in order to bring about the desired behavior change. Ultimately, Diego overcame most of his fear of choking and was able to eat at a more normal pace, which not only resulted in improvement in weight and health but also gave him and his parents much more time away from the table to do things they enjoyed. Diego's symptom of difficulty swallowing still occurred from time to time, but Marco and Elaine learned how to support Diego to eat even when it was challenging. They moved from thinking about Diego's experiences in a binary fashion ("either it is medical or psychological") to focusing on taking effective action to help their child. Ultimately this not only brought about physical recovery but also improvement in Diego's psychological flexibility and coping skills.

In each of these case examples, parents initially were stalled in their efforts to help their child recover because they believed that they, or their child, needed a different kind of help, something that came from outside of the family's resources. In each example, the parents began to make much better progress when they let go of the idea of the solution coming from the outside and instead put all of their effort into tackling the eating disorder behaviors that were happening right in front of them. When parents worked together to address these eating disorder behaviors, every time, every day, many times a day, they began to make true progress. And they each did it in the way that worked for them as a family, a way that fitted with their parenting style—even if was very different to anything they had done before. This allowed each of them to help their child recover from their eating disorder. It also allowed the families to strengthen their relationships and to help their child learn essential coping skills that could allow them to successfully navigate other challenges in life beyond their eating disorders.

Figure 8.1 Why is this so hard? How patience and persistence are the keys to success in FBT
Nandini Datta

8

Why Is This So Hard?: How patience and persistence are the keys to success in FBT

> Doctor, we've been doing everything we can—we eat every meal together, spend hours cooking, monitor our son 24/7, and even pulled him from the soccer team. All this work and he's only gained half a pound in the last month. We're exhausted! FBT is just not working!

Sometimes parents work tirelessly for weeks, meal after meal, to help nourish their child after a period of restricted eating, but just cannot seem to make the needle on the weight scale move. They have watched every meal, snack, and morsel of food their child has eaten over the last few weeks with hawk-like intensity. They have successfully stopped prior restrictive eating disorder behaviors, such as throwing away uneaten school lunches. They have menu planned, grocery shopped, and meal prepped like it is their day job, and in some cases it feels like feeding their child has probably been like a day job, night job, 24/7 job because well right now... it is. Actually, many parents say that helping their child normalize eating patterns is *much harder* than what they do for employment. That is partially because caring for a child with an eating disorder does not have a clock-in and clock-out time, does not take vacations or paid time off, and has no flexibility for sick days. It is also because

DOI: 10.4324/9781003353041-9

the stakes of nourishing a child and reviving or keeping them healthy are so much greater. And lastly this task is personal in a way that keeps parents up all night with worry, adds therapy and medical appointments to already hectic schedules, and can drain the energy out of every family member. Unlike a job, parents do not have the option to quit. In fact, parents are the only ones with the skills, position, and ability to do this particular job.

It is not uncommon for parents to think "Yes, yes, we know we're our child's best chance at beating the eating disorder, and we're trying very hard, but it's just not working." This is a common pitfall that parents can find themselves in, particularly in the first few weeks or months of treatment. Parents may be aligned and feel empowered to tackle the challenges of the eating disorder, but weight gain or behavioral changes in binge eating or purging or increasing food choices is slow to non-existent, despite parental efforts. For parents feeling stuck in the "all pain and no change" vortex, read on to learn more about common barriers that might be getting in the way.

This chapter focuses on what happens when parents work hard to intervene against their child's eating disorder, but have not yet done quite enough to make the crucial difference for progress to full recovery. This chapter will also explain why, for cases where a young person is underweight, it is important for parents to focus on providing their child with calorically dense foods (e.g., cheeseburger and fries and chocolate milkshake rather than steamed fish and vegetables). It also highlights the importance of being consistent around food intake to achieve weight gain and behavioral progress. Parents often commonly believe that they need a dietitian or a meal plan to appropriately nourish their child. In practice though, parents are usually best positioned to make decisions together around what and how to feed their child because they're the ones cooking and serving meals—so doing this and being consistent does not necessarily require a formal meal plan, and in practice such plans may even hinder efforts over time. Even if weight gain per se is not the goal of treatment as it may not be for young people with BN, BED, and ARFID, parents must consistently act against eating disorder behavior patterns, rather than occasionally preventing a behavior. Inconsistent enforcement of behaviors will likely lead only to arguments (and burnout!) and not to effective changes.

Cheeseburgers, Fries, and Milkshakes—Oh My!

I'm not comfortable feeding my child fast food and desserts. Isn't grilled chicken and broccoli healthier for my child than a cheeseburger and fries? Can I just feed them those foods?

Parents frequently ask this question. And the answer is—*it depends*. If a child is avoiding foods that contain fats and carbohydrates due to anxiety or fear of weight gain, or if a child is feeling dizzy or lightheaded due to poor food intake, then the cheeseburger and fries may be in fact what that child's body needs in that moment. If a child is avoiding these foods in fear that they could trigger a binge eating episode, then providing support and monitoring while also incorporating these foods into their diet may be very helpful in overcoming the eating disorder. If weight gain is needed, a child might have to eat many plates of broccoli to even get close to what they might need in terms of calories/energy intake. Not to mention digesting the extra volume in bulky foods with low calorie/energy is often difficult, unpleasant, and painful.

Parents often strive for a nutritional healthy balance in the food they prepare for and offer their children. Society consistently sends messages around the dangers of childhood obesity, and advertising (and social media!) continue to glorify the pursuit of the "thin ideal" and diet culture. In the context of recovery from an eating disorder, it may be confusing to understand how best to promote "health" in the midst of these messages. For a child who is underweight and experiencing negative medical outcomes because of mal-nutrition, increasing overall energy intake is the goal. This is not the time to worry about eating five servings of fruits and vegetables every day when someone's heart rate is so low that they may need an inpatient hospitaliza-tion to stabilize it. Rather, in these moments, what is needed is for that child to regularly consume a surplus of calories to limit further damage to their bodies and brains.

For parents feeling that their child is stuck with weight progress, consider adding more calorie-dense foods throughout the day. Calorie-dense foods are foods that contain a lot of energy (calories) in a small amount, so the body receives a greater amount of energy from less volume. For some people with eating disorders like AN or BN, calorie-dense foods can cause a lot of anxiety and worry, and might be labeled as "bad" or "forbidden foods" due to fears that consuming these types of foods will cause weight gain—which is indeed one of the benefits of them when a person is underweight. Individuals with eating disorders may often feel guilty (like they did something wrong) by eating these types of foods. For young people with ARFID, certain foods may incite higher levels of anxiety, whether due to unfamiliar or non-preferred textures or concerns about choking, vomiting, or other aversive outcomes. That is why children suffering from eating disorders need the help of their parents to approach these foods and feel more comfortable eating them. When food is restricted over time, this leads to difficulties digesting food because the gastrointestinal (GI) system has slowed down as the quantity of food and liquids has decreased as the disorder advanced. This results in what is called a delay in gastric emptying and/or slowing of gut motility. These changes in the GI system can result in pain after eating. For parents, there may be supportive tools that can help lessen the child's post-prandial discomfort, such as heating packs, essential oils, or distractions after meals/snacks. However, eating is the very medicine needed to fix this discomfort, though it can take days, weeks, or months to resolve fully. So it is important not to stop feeding the child even if there are stomach complaints as long as those complaints are the results of the GI system's normal re-adjustment after food restriction. Parents should talk to their pediatrician about this when there are any questions related to GI discomfort.

If parents can temporarily suspend their typical beliefs of what is considered "healthy" with regards to eating and exercise while their child is in active treatment for an eating disorder, they will likely be able to think more flexibly and more easily provide the help their child so desperately needs. Even if, in general, desserts may be seen as non-nutritional, unhealthy, and "bad" nutrition modeling, when a child needs to gain weight, adding a dessert to mealtimes can help challenge eating disorder cognitions as well as provide needed nutrients and fats to the child's diet. Even making what seem like small changes, like switching out non-fat yogurt for full-fat or Greek yogurt, or adding a caloric drink to mealtimes like milk or lemonade, can make big changes in reaching weight targets without adding volumes to the child's daily food intake. Other strategies might include serving butter with bread or cooking with olive oil to make sure that dietary fats are available to help with both weight gain and healthy development. Smoothies and milkshakes are great supplements to meals and snacks so that more calories can be consumed easily and quickly. Incorporating sauces and spreads, such as mayonnaise, guacamole, sour cream, and aioli, also accomplish this goal. Less volume means less chewing and less time spent at a meal or snack. It also increases the chance that a child with an eating disorder will be able to eat the range and types of food they will need to help them progress on their recovery journey.

One quick note about incorporating more energy-dense foods. It is not recommended that parents hide or sneak foods into their child's food. Sometimes parents say that they are "sneaking" extra calories into their child's foods to help with weight gain but they do not want to fight with the child about it, so they do not tell them what they are doing. For example, adding tablespoons of coconut oil to smoothies, pouring cream into hot chocolate, or refilling fat-free milk cartons with full-fat milk, all without telling their child. Unfortunately, this can play into avoidance of fears of foods rather than providing an opportunity to help the child face these fears and anxieties, which they will need to do in order to normalize eating. It is necessary for these "exposures" to be clear and in the open for them to be effective. In addition, children in FBT will have a much smoother transition into phase 2 if they know what and how much they have been eating. Clinical experience has shown that this purposeful deception by parents results in more conflict and can make recovery take much longer.

Avoiding Challenging (Feared) Foods

> Our daughter Sam refuses to eat yogurt or ice cream if it's not fat-free. We've been buying the fat-free versions to have at home. We also found these sugar-free cookies at the store that Sam likes. We have regular ice cream and desserts in the house for our other children; it's just that Sam likes the taste of the fat-free ones better. So we buy those for her to eat. If we go out for ice cream, she just waits until we get home to eat her ice cream. It's sad that she misses out on family ice cream outings, but at least she's eating ice cream!

It is not uncommon for young people with eating disorders to start avoiding certain foods, particularly in the case of AN and BN—foods high in calories, fats, sugars, or carbohydrates. In the beginning of treatment, it may be too difficult for parents to help their children gain weight and stop eating disorder behaviors while also exposing children to avoided foods and helping them overcome this fear. Yet, at some point this becomes an important focus of treatment and a necessary part of helping a child fully recover from an eating disorder. There is a danger that maintaining or adhering to the strict and irrational rules of the eating disorder risks perpetuating the abnormal cognitions and beliefs that are a big part of the problem. Providing the same "safe" meals, even though these food items are tolerated more easily, risks making things harder in the long run. Work with treatment providers to help clarify when and how to increase a variety of foods—particularly foods that are being actively avoided as part of the eating disorder. Young people with eating disorders likely cannot do this on their own, otherwise they would be doing it already. Repeated exposure to these feared foods will, over time, allow their brain to learn that nothing "bad" will happen and they will become more comfortable and less anxious with eating. Some parents hope something is better than nothing, but sometimes holding on to that hope can become a problem:

Oh, I didn't ask Johnny to eat his pasta or bread at dinner—I was just so relieved he was willing to eat salad. And even asked for a second bowl of salad! I wish it had dressing on it though.

Unfortunately, unless that salad includes a large portion of protein, cheese, nuts, and full-calorie dressing, it is not likely to help Johnny gain weight and restore his health. And it might make his eating-disordered beliefs stronger because Johnny feels he successfully avoided foods that he feared. And it reinforces the misguided eating-disordered idea that foods with greater energy density, such as pasta or bread, should be feared and avoided. None of these feelings or experiences actually help Johnny to overcome the eating disorder.

Some parents—when their child has refused to eat much of anything and is losing weight—may feel so relieved that their child is willing to eat even a bite that they find it difficult to push for full meals. Unfortunately, this often prevents adequate nutrition intake, and may even result in weight loss. This mentality of "something is better than nothing" can often get parents stuck in their efforts to battle the eating disorder. For children with ARFID specifically, serious nutritional deficits can occur when diets are severely limited and restricted. In extreme cases, scurvy, anemia, or other diseases may occur due to the limited intake.

It is up to parents to find a way to help their child eat more than just "something" by using consistent and supportive behavioral strategies that include warmth and compassion about how hard this is for their child to do. At the same time, parents cannot give in to the irrational demands and anxieties that their child experiences as a result of their eating disorder. Staying with only a little "something" is dangerous, as it delays a return to health and adds strength to eating-disordered fears. Normalization of eating-related thoughts and fears starts with weight gain and eating feared foods and only after that can these irrational beliefs and anxieties really diminish. To be successful, parents need to overcome this challenge and work with their treatment team to find and implement effective strategies to promote increased, balanced nutrition for their child to combat the wills of the eating disorder.

Exercise for Mental Health

Bianca feels so much calmer and more relaxed when she goes for a daily run. We know the medical team has advised against it, but it makes her so much happier. She used to run every day for an hour after school for cross country practice. She only runs for 30 minutes now. And she says it helps her to eat better on days when she runs. Isn't that the goal—to help her with eating? Especially if it makes her feel better?

Exercise has great benefits for physical and mental health. Of course, parents want their children to exercise and play sports, especially if they love doing these things. Early in treatment, it can be tempting to allow children with eating disorders to continue to exercise or practice their sport, even if the medical professionals have cautioned against it. Perhaps the child is telling everyone that they feel better when they exercise. Or they feel less anxious and can eat more if they are allowed to exercise. Be wary of "improved mental health" in these scenarios. It may be possible (and evenly likely) that what is happening is that an individual with an eating disorder "feels better" because they can act on their eating disorder behaviors. These are often strategies that children with AN and BN employ because they are "less anxious" as they are not battling their compulsion to exercise but rather giving in to it. Or they are "less worried" about eating because they plan to burn off all the calories with exercise. This is important to understand, even if the amount and intensity of the exercise cannot realistically result in weight loss, the psychological compulsion and compensatory nature of this behavior can maintain the eating disorder. Introducing or allowing exercise before someone is physically and mentally ready can be a very slippery slope.

In addition, increased exercise and activity can make weight gain goals harder to achieve. Children who are at a low weight, regardless of the cause, will need to eat even more than what might be expected if they are playing sports, exercising, or engaging in excess movement. This means that parents will need to be even more aware of the amount of activity their child is engaging in and supplement with additional food to cover the energy expenditure. This may be very challenging for a child that already has a low appetite or struggles to take in enough food. In these situations, parents may consider limiting activity to help the body be more restful and gain weight, particularly early on in treatment when the increases in food intake may be harder until the young person is more used to the larger portions and consistent meal schedule.

It is important to communicate to children that *any exercise restrictions are temporary*. Parents should work closely alongside the therapist and medical providers to re-introduce exercise as safely as possible. Once cleared to exercise from a medical standpoint, discuss this in FBT sessions to ensure that adding exercise will not interfere with disrupting eating disorder behaviors.

Also, it is almost always a good idea to provide monitoring or supervision of exercise behaviors, particularly early in treatment. Time alone with exercise equipment or on a walk/run can be very tempting for the child with an eating disorder to give in to the wish to over-exercise. For example, parents are often surprised to discover that their child was running laps (sometimes to the point of exhaustion) during their 15-minute daily walk. Parents may find that accompanying their child during medically cleared exercise allows for enough additional structure that will then keep over-exercising thoughts and behaviors managed. Exercise restrictions may also be implemented due to serious health risks that overexertion poses for the body. In those instances, supervision is paramount to ensure that no harm comes to the young person (e.g., passing out while exercising, falling down and breaking bones, cardiac arrest, etc.) or that help is immediately available, should it be needed.

Consistency Is Key

> On some days, my parents ask me to eat an afterschool snack. On other days, they forget or don't make me eat one. Am I supposed to have an afterschool snack? Do I have to? What if I'm not feeling hungry? I didn't have to eat an afterschool snack before I started FBT. I'm just not sure what I'm supposed to do!

Just because a young person with an eating disorder has an easier time eating one day (or one meal) does not mean that the next meal or snack will go just as smoothly. It is important *not* to be lulled into a false sense of security that the eating disorder is retreating (or gone!) quickly. Sometimes it may appear that the child is doing well, and of course parents hope this will persist, but it is important to be vigilant because deception is one of the behaviors common to most eating disorders at least some of the time. Particularly early on, staying alert and providing consistent levels of support in disrupting eating disorder behaviors is necessary. In addition, children with eating disorders respond well to predictability, routine, and structure even if initially they resist them. While flexibility in eating is often a long-term goal of treatment—because ultimately it is important to be able to eat a wide variety of foods in different contexts with different people—changing the rules can lead to confusion, resistance, and treatment setbacks. For example, if an adolescent is allowed to replace a high-calorie dessert, like a brownie, with a lower calorie option, like an apple, on some days but not others, this can lead to uncertainty about expectations in the future and allows the eating-disordered thoughts and worries to worsen. Or if a child is expected to finish 100% of their meal at one parent's home, but does not have to when at another parent's home, these inconsistent expectations can lead to more conflicts and increased resistance to eating. Be mindful of when expectations for recovery-related behaviors are changed or altered. Do negotiations happen more frequently at breakfast when there are time pressures about making it to work or school? Or perhaps it's harder to ask dinner to be finished after a long, grueling day at the office? Reflect on these situations and work together as a parenting team to ensure consistency.

Therapists understand that constantly monitoring to make sure children are not engaging in eating disorder behaviors is exhausting! However, inconsistently enforcing expectations is likely going to result in recovery taking *longer* at best, and may actually *decrease* the chances in many cases. Such inconsistency allows the eating-related thoughts and behaviors to re-emerge and strengthen the very behaviors everyone is working so hard to stop. Unfortunately, there are no shortcuts in a process that must regularly and predictably challenge the eating disorder. Recovery is hard. The goal is to make it hard for the shortest amount of time.

Does My Child Need to See a Dietitian?

> How can my child recover from an eating disorder without a meal plan?
> How many calories does my child need to regain the weight they lost?
> I am not an expert in food! I don't know what my child needs to eat.

One of the more common questions that parents have during FBT is whether their child should see a dietitian. While on the surface it might seem that meeting with a dietitian would help them recover faster—and sometimes dieticians can be a great help—most families in FBT are successful without adding a dietician into the mix. Sometimes, adding a dietitian to the treatment team may inadvertently make recovery harder and take longer. Most parents already have all the knowledge and expertise needed to feed their child when they are well. Parents know from experience that children will gain weight faster if they eat food with more energy and calories. Cheeseburgers and milkshakes will get someone to their target weight range much faster than kale and strawberries. Although fruits and vegetables provide many important nutrients to the body, these foods are not going to promote weight gain at the rate needed to restore health for a young person that is underweight. Parents are likely just as concerned if their child only eats carrots as they would be if their child only ate pizza. Parents understand that a balance in foods is needed.

Meal plans and calorie goals are not standard interventions in FBT. These tools, which are sometimes introduced as a way to help with eating, can actually lead to unnecessary conflicts (the meal plan vs. the parent's prepared meal) and perpetuate "safe eating" ideations with the rules and inflexibility of the eating disorder. In these cases, it can be very difficult to stop using meal plans once they are introduced, and they can become vehicles for reinforcing rigid control over the young person's eating habits. Most children and adolescents do not follow a structured meal plan or calorie count even if they follow general guidelines in their diet. Moreover, sticking with a structured meal plan can be quite challenging for families to implement, and over time what seemed helpful because the plan "told parents what to do" actually becomes a crutch that adds unnecessary stress to parents. Families are likely already overwhelmed with the task of nourishing an ill child, stopping behaviors like over-exercising or purging, providing emotional support to the child suffering with an eating disorder, and caring for everyone in the family. Take the following example of a situation that happened for Caitlin and her family.

Caitlin was a 15-year-old female diagnosed with AN. Before starting FBT, she had a week-long stay at an inpatient medical stabilization unit due to low heart rate because of restriction and malnutrition. Caitlin and her family progressed well in the first month of FBT, with Caitlin's weight increasing each week and her family noticing less resistance at mealtimes. However, her weight gain began to plateau. When discussing meals and snacks in the FBT session, the therapist learned that Caitlin was eating "ants on a log" (celery stick with peanut butter and raisins) every day for an afternoon snack. Caitlin shared that she hated this snack and never liked to eat it, even before the eating disorder. Her parents agreed that this was not a typical food usually served in their family. However, since this snack was part of an example meal plan given to the family during their inpatient stay, the parents kept making Caitlin this snack every day at home. When asked, Caitlin identified many different snacks she'd rather have, all of which contained more calories and fats than the "ants on a log." The family thought that they had to stick to the meal plan—which was intended only for educational purposes as an example—in order to help their daughter recover from AN. Once the therapist explained that the family did not have to follow the meal plan (or any meal plan), her parents were able to work together to identify a variety of snack options that were not only more preferrable to Caitlin, but also helped her move forward with weight gain. And these snacks were options that Caitlin would choose herself during phase 2 of treatment, which helped better prepare her to take back the responsibility of eating.

Recovery from an eating disorder is hard work. It often involves all family members working together for the same unified goals. It can also take a lot of time and energy. Families in treatment may already feel maxed out with therapy and medical appointments. Adding another appointment with another professional on another day in another location can stress an already overtaxed system. If the dietitian is not already working on the treatment team, then there can be extra coordination efforts on parents to relay information between providers—or consolidate information if answers conflict! As the saying goes, too many cooks spoil the broth.

Usually parents are best positioned to work together to serve and provide foods for their family. After all, parents have been feeding their children their whole lives. Eating disorders do not develop because parents don't know what types of foods to give their children. Similarly, a child's eating disorder does not happen because they are confused about what foods to eat. Treatment for eating disorders does not entail learning more about the macronutrient profile of foods or changing the way families typically eat. If recovery from an eating disorder was possible by simply following a meal plan, that would be great, but there is no evidence that meal plans are consistently helpful or increase recovery, especially in children. Recovery requires the child to eat a range of foods, flexibly, in the environments they live in (homes, schools, friends' homes, etc.). Meal plans are not flexible enough or "normal" enough to achieve these goals.

At the same time, parents should know that dietitians are incredibly skilled professionals with a detailed knowledge base of nutrition. For children with chronic medical illnesses, food allergies, GI conditions, diabetes, and other endocrine system disorders, dieticians can provide a wealth of knowledge, skill, support, and instruction on how best to nourish the body for optimal health. In contrast, most children with eating disorders do not also have these co-occurring conditions. Their bodies can use and store nutrients without issue. Thus, children with eating disorders often do not need a specialized diet plan. It is recommended that in FBT consultations with dietitians are parent-only and do not include the young person with the eating disorder.

In addition, dietitians should have experience working with eating disorders and a basic understanding of FBT. One final note—none of the research-based randomized clinical trials (gold-standard research design) testing FBT for adolescents with AN, BN, or ARFID included dietitians. This means that hundreds of families going through FBT found a way to nourish their child and disrupt eating disorder behaviors without meeting with a dietitian.

When Pushing Through the Pain in AN Is Necessary to Be Successful in FBT

Cecilia was an 18-year-old female of Mexican American descent with AN, who presented to FBT after a two-week stay at an inpatient medical stabilization unit for bradycardia and orthostasis. She presented to treatment with her married parents and younger brother. Cecilia began restricting her food intake approximately one year prior to the hospitalization, and lost significant weight in the process. Although her parents understood the severity of her illness and the need to regain weight (Cecilia needed 25 pounds to be back within the excepted range for her age and height), they did not feel comfortable pushing her to eat feared foods. For example, Cecilia ate sugar-free, fat-free packaged protein bars as dessert, whereas the rest of her family ate cookies and ice cream. She was unable to eat the cake served on her 18th birthday. By providing only foods the patient felt comfortable eating (e.g., lean meats, whole grains, vegetables, fruits), her parents were able to help her gain about 10 pounds over the course of several months. However, Cecilia remained just as fearful to try foods outside of this narrow range. She was unable to eat at restaurants with her family without significant distress. Furthermore, Cecilia still needed another 15 pounds of weight gain to get back to her expected target and had not had a menstrual cycle in over a year.

At this point several months into treatment, her parents reported feeling burnt out, exhausted, and tired of constantly preparing and monitoring meals. They felt relieved that Cecilia was no longer in medical danger of being hospitalized and were grateful that she was at least eating three meals a day. The family contemplated ending treatment and allowing Cecilia to just eat the foods she wanted (consistent with the wishes of her AN). Instead, with the support of their therapist, Cecilia and her parents identified Cecilia's feared foods and made plans for her parents to introduce them throughout the week. This was extremely hard at first, as Cecilia's parents had difficulty tolerating her distress and felt burnt out from their re-nourishment efforts. Eventually, after weeks of continued efforts to eat more feared foods, Cecilia made progress in incorporating a wider range of foods into her diet. Her weight gain continued, albeit more slowly, and she maintained improved vital sign stability. She was even able to eat at a restaurant and choose pasta (a previously avoided fear food) during a family celebration dinner.

Cecilia's continued progress towards recovery from AN would not have been possible without her parents deciding to regroup and refocus efforts on this goal. This was not without great difficulty and strife for Cecilia and her parents. However, Cecilia's parents realized that they did not want their daughter to be "part-way" better from an ED. Just because she was not back in the hospital did not mean that she was in a place of health, physically or mentally. Cecilia's parents decided to dig deep into their already exhausted reserves to find ways to help Cecilia battle a very stuck part of her eating disorder.

When Pushing Through the Pain Is Necessary in FBT for BN

Abigail was a 16-year-old female with a diagnosis of BN in FBT living with her married parents and younger sister. Prior to the start of FBT, Abigail was skipping breakfast and lunch, purging (self-induced vomiting) multiple times during the day, and experiencing binge eating episodes once or twice each week. Due to the family's busy schedules, her parents had not noticed that Abigail was skipping meals and purposefully restricting food intake. They were also unaware of the binge eating or purging behaviors. The parents were then quite shocked when Abigail's vital signs and blood work from her annual well-child checkup indicated possible purging. Abigail was referred to an eating disorders clinic and began FBT shortly after receiving a diagnosis of BN.

Abigail's parents worked together to ensure constant supervision and monitoring of breakfast and dinner. They decided to restrict bathroom use for 30 minutes after meals. Her parents also asked Abigail to start taking showers in the morning rather than at night, which had been a frequent time for purging before starting treatment. Initially, her parents decided not to monitor lunchtime at school, due to work schedules and previous commitments.

Abigail did well during the first four weeks of treatment. She decreased her purging episodes from daily to less than once per week, established a consistent eating pattern, and decreased binge eating episodes. She was even able to start making her own breakfast and needing less supervision around eating. Although she was able to decrease purging and binge eating, these behaviors persisted, albeit much less than previously. When discussing additional supports to help Abigail reach abstinence of the eating disorder behaviors, it became clear that she needed more support during lunchtime at school. Abigail acknowledged that she occasionally still threw out her pre-packed lunch, which then often led to a binge eating episode (and subsequent purging) later that same day.

Upon learning this, her parents felt frustrated and annoyed with Abigail. They wanted her to manage eating during the school day, as they were providing such close supervision the rest of the time. As the family, therapist, and Abigail worked together in the FBT sessions, her parents began to realize that additional support during the lunchtime at school was needed after all. Abigail's mother decided to take leave from her job to pick up Abigail during lunch and eat together. This also allowed Abigail's mother to provide support and distractions right after the meal to prevent Abigail from purging. Abigail's mother was able to work it out with her employer to only miss one and a half hours of work during the day, which allowed her to maintain her employment and benefits while also providing additional care for Abigail. This extra support resulted in abstinence of binge eating and purging episodes for Abigail. After a few weeks, Abigail no longer needed her mother to eat lunch with her, and she began to transition to phase 2 of treatment without the resurgence of binge eating and purging.

Parental consistency in monitoring all meals/snacks and high-risk times for purging was key in helping Abigail decrease eating-disordered behaviors quickly. This consistency and vigilance early on also likely shortened the course of overall treatment. It may not always be possible for parents to take a leave of absence from work or time away, even though many employers are legally mandated to allow employees to do so in order to care for themselves or a sick family member. In these instances, it is helpful to think creatively about the available support people in a family's circle. Can the child eat with a teacher or another trusted adult at school? Or is the child able to video-call a parent during meals when they are apart? Are there extended family members that can monitor the child for breakfast or dinner time if work or other obligations, such as taking care of another family member, impact a parent's ability to do so? It truly takes a village, and helping a child recover from an ED is no exception!

When It Is Necessary to Push Through Pain in FBT for ARFID

Josh was a 7-year-old boy with low-weight ARFID who presented to FBT following a referral from his pediatrician due to concerns about poor growth. Although Josh had always been on the smaller size for his age, he recently fell off his growth chart and was now in the 1st percentile for height and weight. Josh's parents were recently divorced; he primarily lived with his mother but stayed at his father's house every other weekend. Both parents attended FBT sessions. Early on in FBT, his parents decided to implement a reward system to help Josh increase his energy intake. For every meal that Josh completed, he would earn a sticker that could be cashed in for a reward once he accumulated enough stickers. Week after week, Josh would earn a large number of stickers, which he then turned into rewards such as new toys and video games. Yet Josh had not gained any weight since the start of treatment.

During an individual check-in time with his FBT therapist, Josh shared that he no longer wanted to go to his father's house on the weekends. When asked why, Josh said it was because his father required him to finish 100% of his meals before he earned a sticker, whereas his mother gave him a sticker for taking at least one bite of all the food served at a meal. The FBT therapist was then able to have a discussion with the family in session around clarifying expectations for food intake at different houses, which helped the family all agree on a detailed plan as to how and when Josh could earn stickers towards his reward chart. By the next session, Josh only had half the stickers he had previously earned in a week. However, he had gained a pound. With some continued refinement of the reward system and frequent reminders about consistency across households in the parents' approach to ARFID, Josh went on to gain another 10 pounds and added a handful of new foods into his diet.

This case illustrates a familiar challenge in FBT—not just difficulties in parental alignment (for more on this, please read Chapter 3), but also the importance of consistency in expectations around eating. Staying consistent in the expectations from the very start of treatment can help promote health faster, lessen conflict, and prevent parent (and child!) burnout in the process. For anyone having difficulties in this area, rest assured it is a common experience, and FBT therapists should be well equipped to help families navigate these and similar challenges.

This chapter focused on the need for parents to overcome the challenge of under-feeding, inconsistent feeding, and overdependence on professionally devised interventions about eating like meal plans, and instead, it focused on being confident in their skills and knowledge as parents. In consultation with their FBT therapist, parents make decisions about how they are going to be most successful when navigating the challenge (and pain) of stalled progress.

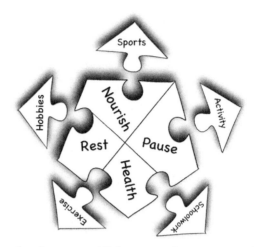

Figure 9.1 Does everything have to stop? Balancing academic progress, athletics, or activities, and ED recovery
Nandini Datta

9
Does Everything Have to Stop?: Balancing academic progress, athletics, or activities, and ED recovery

> Soccer is the one thing that gives him joy. His self-esteem is so important and he gets a lot of this from his performance on his team. We want him to keep playing because we feel it will help motivate him to recover. It will be so much harder if he can't play.

It is difficult for parents to know what to prioritize as their children navigate their lives. Trying to balance family life, social, academic, and athletic pursuits is a challenge at the best of times. It is so much harder though when an eating disorder complicates all of these important aspects of life—as they

DOI: 10.4324/9781003353041-10

always do. However, it is crucial to overcome this challenge in order to help your child recover from an eating disorder effectively and efficiently. It is easy to say that addressing the eating disorder takes precedence over everything else, but it is much harder for parents to act on this because of their ambivalence and uncertainty about this kind of dictum. It is also true that even in the most dire health situation, parents cannot simply ignore their child's need for social, academic, athletic, family, and physical activities. Indeed, if a child is hospitalized with a medical illness, for example, the immediate need for physical health treatments will take priority, but parents and caregivers know from experience that one cannot have this limited focus or the child's overall health and recovery will likely be compromised. Balance is needed.

Let's start to try and help with this dilemma by discussing the role of family, social, academic, and athletic activities in overall development in a bit more detail to illustrate why they are important. By doing so, we can help to identify their respective place in helping children to grow and develop. By understanding this a bit more it may help parents to determine better how to value or balance their relative importance in the context of treatment for an eating disorder. It may also help to identify ways parents can support these other areas in alternative ways during FBT for their child's eating disorder without compromising the effectiveness and outcome of treatment.

Participation in family life is one of the ways that children and adolescents develop a secure base from which to navigate in the larger social world. In early life, families provide concrete forms of protections and nurture (shelter, warmth, food, love, safety). As children age families continue to provide these basics of course, but the family unit is also itself a dynamic organization where relationships and activities shape the developing young person. In simple terms, family processes and activities are important in helping children learn about groups. Parents have authority and control over most family decisions, but depending on the family, this authority may be shared as children grow and develop capacities to share responsibility. Connections to larger cultural processes are also part of what families do—through participation in religion, politics, communities, and cultural/ethnic identity-affirming activities. Families also develop their own internal processes that support one another through shared recreational activities, family vacations, and family holiday traditions. Eating disorders almost always cause severe disruptions in the young person's family leading to challenges in maintaining connections to other family members, often leading to frustration, anxiety, and fear for some, and withdrawal and isolation in many. One of the first things many parents of a young person with AN might notice is the withdrawal from mealtimes by the young person, often soon followed by self-isolation and decreased interaction with siblings. Similarly, binge eating and purging behaviors often lead to attempts to hide or deceive other family members so that these behaviors will go unnoticed. This in turn leads to diminished trust and connection with the family and increases the isolation of the young person. For ARFID, the lack of interest in eating, the extreme pickiness, and the fears about eating create ongoing struggles for families who want to eat together and share mealtimes as part of supporting connections and reinforcing nurture and care.

Social activities for children and adolescents are important from a developmental perspective for several reasons. First, social activities help children learn to communicate with others and this helps them to learn to work better with others to achieve common goals—a life skill that will make them more successful overall. Socialization is also intrinsically rewarding for most (but not all) children and leads to an overall sense of belonging to a group and helps promote confidence and self-esteem. Eating disorders interfere with socialization regardless of the behavioral or cognitive characteristics of the specific diagnosis. For ARFID, the extreme pickiness, the lack of energy, and anxiety about eating often keep these children from participating in common social activities like birthday parties, sleepovers, and camps. Although most children with AN functioned fairly well socially before they became ill, the psychological distress and cognitive and behavioral preoccupations of the disorder often lead to anxiety in social situations, especially when eating is involved, and social and emotional withdrawal from friends and family is a very common result. Binge eating and Bulimia Nervosa also cause social problems as they lead to secretive eating and a wish to hide compensatory behaviors when they are present.

School is important for children and adolescents as the skills they need to master to compete for college and work are taught there. Academic mastery increases capacity for engagement with meaningful ideas and helps to identify and build specific intellectual skills that are necessary building blocks for a successful life. However, eating disorders interfere with learning in important ways. With AN academic performance is usually excellent prior to the illness and is often preserved late into the course of the disorder. This often gives the illusion that the young person with AN is managing well and their judgment is sound. This is true to a certain extent, but not when eating and weight are concerned. However, over time, the preoccupations and driven behaviors have a dulling effect on the mind and body making learning and academic performance increasingly challenging. At its most severe, starvation-related malnutrition can lead to an obtunded mental state of profound proportions. Binge eating and purging behaviors and related distorted cognitions can also negatively impact academic performance in a variety of ways. The binge eating or binge-purge cycle interferes with normal physiology, including concentration and the ability to focus. Both binge eating and purging can lead to dissociative states that make learning almost impossible. Children with ARFID are often hungry or do not recognize their physiologic need to eat. This leads to disruptive behaviors and inattention in the classroom and often results in poor school performance.

Many children and adolescents are involved in youth sports. Athletic participation often combines both social and physical activities. However, unlike general socialization, athletic socialization is usually more focused on a specific shared activity or in the case of team sports, on shared and/or complementary competencies leading to achieving a shared goal—winning at something. Eating disorders erode both the social and performance aspects of sports participation and lead to a diminishing of the benefits of participation. In some cases this is ironic because some eating disorders emerge in the context of endeavors to improve athletic performance by dieting, over-exercising, or taking substances to lose or gain weight or musculature. Children with ARFID are often unable to fully participate in sports because of low energy, poor growth, lack of strength, and generally poor nutrition. For AN, the drive to improve athletic performance can lead to self-injurious over-exercise and vulnerability to bone fractures due to loss of bone mass. For some sports, like wrestling, making weight is a challenge and intermittent severe restriction can lead to binge eating and purging behaviors.

So, it is clear that all these important other activities—family life, academic, social and athletic—are very important to supporting healthy development. This is exactly why parents often struggle in FBT to find a way to balance the needs for treatment for the eating disorder and these other important factors. We discuss below how parents struggled with this challenge and overcame it in the context of FBT.

How Failure to Find the Right Balance Between Other Activities (Athletics) and Treatment Interferes With Progress in FBT for AN

Bertrand was 16 when he began restricting his eating after he broke his ankle playing soccer. He was the older of two highly competitive brothers whose mother stayed at home to care for them and whose father was the CFO of a moderately sized tech firm. Bertrand was a relatively shy and quiet boy who kept most of his thoughts and feelings to himself. He was smaller than his younger brother but was the more athletic of the two. He excelled at soccer in particular and was hoping to play at the D1 college level. When he broke his ankle in a scrimmage, he was concerned about losing his "fitness" so started dieting to prevent weight gain. He became increasingly fat conscious, checking his abs in particular repeatedly throughout the day by pinching and examining them in the mirror. He weighed himself four to six times a day. He reduced his intake to proteins in small amounts and also tried to exercise without using his affected ankle whenever he could. He lost 20 pounds in several weeks on an already very lean frame and required hospitalization for a low heart rate. When he was discharged, his parents rather reluctantly started FBT. They were concerned that Bertrand would "fight them" all the way as they knew him to be very determined. They also worried about his younger brother participating because Bertrand would be embarrassed by his presence. As soon as he was discharged from hospital, Bertrand demanded to return to soccer practice. By this point, his ankle was out of a cast and his orthopedics physicians recommended slow resumption of activities to strengthen the muscles in the leg. In discussions with the FBT therapist, the family asserted that for Bertrand it was going to be essential that he play soccer again as soon as possible because that would motivate him to eat and get stronger again. While the therapist supported the *goal* of Bertrand playing soccer as soon as he was weight restored and able to eat enough to maintain health and growth, the therapist cautioned that resuming competitive practice too soon might jeopardize his progress and could land him back in the hospital. As expected, Bertrand was unrelenting in his demand to play soccer and his parents succumbed to his pleading and threats. Bertrand was soon practicing almost at full effort but he did not gain weight and became easily exhausted and could not play at his typical high level. He was stuck in the worries and anxieties that AN brought to him and his participation in soccer at this point only worsened things for him. He felt he was a failure at soccer and he was still not eating enough to regain the weight he had lost.

This situation is all too common when an athlete develops AN. Their drive to perform is high and while this competitiveness is an asset when they are healthy, it unfortunately undermines their ability to make progress when AN is present. Parents can help with this dilemma, but it requires them to find and articulate a balance between the immediate needs for nutrition, rest, and recovery from AN and the longer-term benefits of playing sport in their child's physical and emotional development. Sometimes parents are just as invested in the sports achievements of their children or even more so than the child themselves. When this happens, it can make it even harder to make the right decisions about prioritizing and balancing treatment for AN and playing sport.

> After several weeks of poor weight gain and increasing awareness on the parents part, they met with the soccer coach to discuss how to help Bertrand. The coach was sympathetic to the parents and cared about Bertrand, one of his top players. He met with Bertrand and told him he could not practice with the team, but could attend practices as an assistant coach to help the other players develop their skills until his own weight and strength returned to normal.

Bertrand's parents ultimately found a way to balance the immediate need for him to be involved in soccer with less negative effects on his eating and weight by deciding together to discuss the situation with his coach. By involving the coach, the parents helped Bertrand to accept the decision and the coach's strategy to use Bertrand's skills to help others was a successful one. Although Bertrand continued to struggle to eat enough for several more months, his acceptance of the need for limited sports participation and his parents' insistence on limiting his activity ultimately helped him make the progress he needed to recover and again play soccer when he was well.

How Failure to Find the Right Balance Between Activities (Socialization) and Treatment Interferes in FBT for Binge Eating and BN

> Nadia was a highly social 16-year-old who was always seen as an extra-verted and outgoing personality. However, as she entered her junior year of high school, Nadia became increasingly concerned about her weight. She had spent the summer working at a kids' sleepover camp and had eaten more that she usually would have at home. She gained about 10 pounds and when she returned home decided to go on a diet. She tried not to eat in the morning and very little at midday. She began

losing weight but she also had increasing impulses to eat and after several weeks she began to eat uncontrollably is the afternoons after school when no one was around, or she would get up in the night and binge eat when everyone else in the family was sleeping. Her weight again increased and this made Nadia feel that she was a failure. Her exhaustion from her irregular eating and her late-night binge eating made her more irritable and sad. Her friends noted something had changed but Nadia was ashamed to tell them about what was going on. She began to withdraw from her many previous activities and volunteer work. When her parents finally discovered what Nadia was doing and sought help, they were more concerned with her personality change and the fact that she had withdrawn from friends—staying at home instead of doing things with friends, avoiding social activities, especially any that involved eating—than they were about her binge eating. She had a good relationship with her parents, but she was ashamed of her behaviors but afraid of giving them up as they had become a way for her to manage her loneliness and isolation as well as her fear of weight gain. When her parents began FBT, they expressed their strong belief that getting Nadia socializing with peers was a necessary first step for her to recover.

The radical change in socialization was a clear and significant problem that was associated with Nadia's binge eating onset. Her parents were correct that increased socialization would likely help Nadia recover; however, it was probably not the best thing to focus on as Nadia stated FBT. As important as Nadia's social life and activities were to her, she was too far removed from being able to use them effectively at this point given the entrenched nature of her cognitive, behavioral, and emotional state related to binge eating.

Fairly quickly in FBT, Nadia's parents were effective in helping her decrease her binge eating by working with her to identify when she was most tempted to binge eat and what foods were most tempting. However, they struggled with Nadia's continued social isolation and worried that she was depressed. They planned a party for her without her knowledge and invited many of the friends she had shunned for months. When they told Nadia about the party, she became upset and ran out of the house threatening to harm herself. Her father chased after her and brought her home, but Nadia refused to attend the party as she claimed she was too fat and too ugly. In the FBT sessions that followed, Nadia reported binge eating more frequently and appeared more depressed. The therapist spent time with Nadia guiding her on how to find a way to help her parents be supportive at this time. Ultimately, she was able to allow them to help her with preventing binge eating episodes again but only if they also let her make decisions about her social life.

In FBT for binge eating and purging, the aim is for the therapist to help the adolescent and parents work together to disrupt these behaviors. This is only possible if the adolescent and parents are aligned and accept the need to collaborate. This is different than FBT for AN where, at least at the start, most adolescents with AN are unable to collaborate as they are not motivated to gain weight. However, in Nadia's case the initial productive collaboration broke down because her parents acted independently to try to effect changes in Nadia's social life that she was unprepared to undertake at that point. In FBT generally, parental management is limited to those areas that are directly affected by the eating disorder behaviors (eating patterns, food choices, compensatory behaviors, food weighing, mirror checking, etc.) and does not extend into other areas of the child's life in an age-inappropriate way. As a 16-year-old, Nadia would be expected to make decisions about who her friends were and what activities she participated in for the most part. Of course her parents might approve or disapprove of some friends and some activities, but part of the job of an adolescent is to learn to make these decisions with increasing independence. With a younger child with an eating disorder, the surprise party the parents planned might have been more acceptable and certainly would have been developmentally more appropriate. Instead, in Nadia's case, the surprise party created a crisis in the alliance between Nadia and her parents and led to a significant setback in her eating disorder symptoms, and extended the treatment. Nonetheless, after Nadia discussed her perspective on all this with her parents in session, they found a way forward.

After several more weeks, Nadia was back on course with very few binge episodes in the past week and her mood was noticeably improved. She also agreed with her parents that she did need to see her friends again, but she needed to start slowly. She suggested going to a movie with the friend she felt most comfortable with and who she had told about her struggles with binge eating. This outing went well and over time Nadia was increasingly eager to spend time with friends again. Her worry about their judgment decreased, as did her anxiety about binge eating in situations when they were out at parties or other social events where some of the foods that were the most challenging were available. She discussed with her parents when these situations arose and asked for their support when she felt she overate. Their continued reassurance helped Nadia to manage her fears of loss of control and helped to decrease her self-criticism when she was sometimes unsuccessful in preventing herself from binge eating.

What's important to understand about Nadia and her family's experience is that trying to focus too soon on socialization ended up being counterproductive for all concerned and put at risk the important progress they had made. In this instance Nadia's parents were able to pivot back to their focus on helping Nadia with her eating disorder symptoms, supporting her emotional growth as she learned to live without binge eating, and to letting her take the lead on when and how to socialize during her recovery process.

How Failure to Find the Right Balance Between Activities (Academic) and Treatment Interferes with FBT for ARFID

Zach was an active 12-year-old boy with ARFID and Attention Deficit Hyperactivity Disorder (ADHD). His ARFID symptoms began early in life. He had trouble transitioning from bottle to solid foods and was averse to trying new foods from an early age. In addition, he had difficulty settling at the table at mealtimes and often wandered off to play instead of eating. Eating was generally a low priority for him. At first his parents and pediatrician were content to hope that Zach would gradually increase the amount he would eat and his range of food choices, but this never happened. Instead, Zach continued to be very thin and by age 12 he had begun to fall off his growth curve. In addition to his ARFID, Zach struggled in school. His parents were both teachers and placed high value on his school performance. Medications (psychostimulants) for ADHD were started when Zach was about 10 years of age and though they helped Zach with his attention and hyperactivity in the mornings, they also appeared to exacerbate his lack of appetite and interest in food or eating. Zach's parents were worried about him but were tired of arguing with him about doing homework, eating, and trying to prevent him from running around disrupting family and school activities. When they started with FBT-ARFID, they were confused, exhausted, and feeling generally helpless.

School achievement is important. Zach was 12 years old and the level of academic challenge and expectation tends to ratchet up at about this time with the emergence of more abstract thinking and reasoning skills. Parents tend to see this "middle school" period as a harbinger of likely future academic success in high school and college—which it certainly can be. Therefore, it is not surprising that Zach's parents were more focused on his poor academic performance than on his low weight and highly selective eating. Although both were serious problems, they had become more accommodating to his ARFID eating patterns, almost accepting trying to change them as a hopeless cause. Nonetheless the pediatrician's alarm about Zach falling off his growth curve incited them to look for treatment for Zach's ARFID. Thus, they started FBT-ARFID with a fair amount of ambivalence and uncertainty about what they could really expect to accomplish.

In the early sessions of FBT-ARFID, Zach's parents struggled to separate the eating behaviors and worries from Zach as a developing young person. He had always been a difficult eater. It was just who he was they thought. In fact though, while Zach's symptoms were longstanding and entrenched, they were not actually *him*—he did not identify with them as a key part of his identity. In fact, he did not really like being so skinny and he was worried about not getting taller. He recognized that ARFID was interfering with his growth and health, but did not know how to work on it. In the opening session of FBT-ARFID, Zach's parents expressed concern for his weight and his physical health, but they were also equally or even more worried about his school performance. He had just failed another math quiz that day. They also said they had been told by the pediatrician that the ADHD medicine was likely making it more difficult for Zach to eat and gain weight, but they were reluctant to change medications because Zach's school work, though still pretty poor, had improved since he'd been taking it. They were genuinely confused about how to proceed. The FBT therapist asked the parents to consider several things: first, Zach was just about to enter his growth spurt as he started puberty and without additional weight gain, the outcome of his linear growth (height) was likely to be suboptimal; next, that although his current medications were helpful, there were other options to help with ADHD and some of them might actually help with weight gain (e.g., serotonin reuptake inhibitors: SSRIs); third, Zach was only starting middle school and he had several years to get back on track with his academic potential; and fourth, that Zach was motivated to try to address his ARFID now because he was eager to grow. Finally, the therapist noted that FBT-ARFID treatment lasted only a few months and that they would either see progress and benefit or not so that they did not have to think of ARFID treatment as something that would take their entire focus for an extended period. At the same time though, the therapist emphasized that even if FBT-ARFID was effective, Zach would continue to need support around combating his ARFID symptoms, and the skills they would learn during treatment would be applicable in the long term.

After the treatment session, Zach's parents discussed what the therapist had said between themselves and then also with Zach. When they returned to treatment the next week, they had agreed that for now they would focus on ARFID and use FBT to help them learn how to be more effective at helping Zach with his eating so he could gain weight and hopefully start growing again. They had also contacted their pediatrician and requested a consultation with a child psychiatrist to explore other medication options for Zach's ADHD. Finding the right balance in Zach's case was initially challenging, but with guidance and consultation, his parents found the right path to start down to insure Zach's health, growth, and ultimately his academic success too.

In each of these case illustrations, the parents' initial urge to focus on other important life pursuits was understandable but also contributed to making recovery from their child's eating disorder more difficult. In each instance, though, the parents found a way to prioritize and balance the adoption of these other important activities in the context of their child's recovery.

Figure 10.1 Don't give up too soon: Why it is important to accomplish the goals of FBT to reduce the likelihood of relapse
Nandini Datta

10

Don't Give Up Too Soon: Why it is important to accomplish the goals of FBT to reduce the likelihood of relapse

> We thought we were in the clear—finish line in sight! We thought the progress she had made was good enough, her weight was high enough, but we were shocked to see how quickly she relapsed… How did this happen?
>
> Parents of a teenaged girl with Bulimia Nervosa

Sometimes after making good, steady progress in FBT a young person may have an unexpected setback or relapse. Eating disorders are difficult to overcome and a young person remains vulnerable to relapse even when symptoms may seem, comparatively speaking, much better. Even if remission is achieved, relapse may always be a possibility. Thus, vigilance to signs of recurring symptoms is important so they can be addressed quickly.

It is not unusual for a young person to experience an uptick in distress when nearing recovery, and parents, reacting to their child's distress and believing that their child is no longer in crisis, sometimes agree to stop pushing for progress. Phrases like "Well, XX pounds is good enough, right?" or "At least they have stopped doing XX, right?" are ones parents sometimes consider

DOI: 10.4324/9781003353041-11

at this juncture. Parents may believe that if progress stops now, it will be a "good enough" outcome, that they've come far enough, their child is at a reasonable weight or has decreased binge eating and purging or is eating a good enough range of foods, but leaving these remnants of the eating disorder in place provides the opportunity for them to worsen again over time. For this reason, even in the last stages of FBT, it is important to remember what we have reviewed in earlier chapters regarding the worries and fears of eating disorders, and how they can lead the young person with an eating disorder to do things that keep the disorder in place—even when everything appears much improved. By this point, parents have been through the worst and the hardest part of helping their child change the behaviors that maintain the eating disorder. Here, parents usually have a full skillset under their belt and have practice using it in phase 1 and the beginning of phase 2 of FBT. However, this is a tiring process, and they might be absolutely exhausted. Moreover, if there are signs of relapse, it might feel defeating to have to dip back into that bag of skills when parents feel as though they and their child have already put in the hard work. That's why it can be tempting to hope that it's "good enough" and back off. However, this is a mistake that some parents make that they later come to regret.

It is sometimes helpful for parents to remind themselves that a relapse is not automatically a marker of poor progress, but, rather, it can actually be evidence of all of the hard work they have done and how far they have come. We know that eating disorder thoughts often worsen as recovery approaches—and just as parents see the light at the end of the tunnel, so does the child with the eating disorder—and this can cause fears and anxieties to heighten. This is stressful for the young person and despite—or rather, *due* to all of the progress they have made—eating disorder-related worries may worsen in the short term. It is important for parents to stay firm in the resolve to attain recovery, overcoming this last hurdle and not stopping too soon. Another metaphor we sometime use is that treating an eating disorder is like climbing a sand dune—you can't stop along the way or you slip back down and just have to make up that climb again with tired muscles. As we have highlighted throughout this book, it is important to stay determined in making sure the young person is on track with their recovery, leaving no room for negotiation or bargaining at any stage of treatment.

So, what happens if things are progressing well and the eating disorder symptoms start re-appearing a little bit? For instance, parents might start to notice that their child is portioning themselves less at meals or skipping snacks—citing "I forgot" when probed. Or more lunch is coming back from school untouched. Or other small behaviors that set off warning bells parents are all too familiar with start recurring—such as large quantities of food going missing again or seeing vomit in the bathroom. For ARFID, the child may start refusing to eat foods again that have been added to their repertoire. It is important here to act quickly and use the skills that have been effective to get parents and families this far. This means watching, warning, and stepping in or intervening. What we mean by this is if parents notice any signs of recurring eating-disordered behaviors and if warning bells are going off, gather some data, consult with a partner if applicable, and make a plan. If it is clear that eating-disordered symptoms are returning, parents might consider moving to the next step—warning. Here, parents will have to determine that what they are seeing is putting their child's health at risk again. Warning will usually involve talking to their child—but this might look different than it did in phase 1. Now, it will be important to decide if it is necessary for parents to take control again or if there are challenges their child is having in managing on their own in phase 2 that they need support around. Conversations will involve pointing out the behaviors parents have noticed and brainstorming with their child around how to correct the behavior. The reason to do this is twofold—the first is to make sure the eating disorder knows parents are still watching and actively supporting recovery. The second is to remind the healthy part of the young person that their parents want to trust them and continue to honor the developmentally appropriate independence they've gained back over the course of phase 2. By letting the young person have the opportunity to correct their behavioral responses and share what they are thinking and how they may do this, it shows parents that their child *is* able to manage some of the independence on their own. Of course, in the case of younger children with ARFID, phase 2 is not only about independent eating, but also about eating enough food and food variety for health and growth. Parents will remain in charge in an age-appropriate way but can still solicit input from their child about why they may be having difficulties and what they think might help them. However, if the conversation suggests that the young person is not currently able to make healthy decisions about eating, then parents should be prepared to step back in or intervene. We discuss below several case examples when parents have struggled with this challenge and worked together and with their therapist to overcome it in the context of FBT.

How Falling at the Last Hurdle Interferes With Progress in FBT for AN

Stella was 18 and a rising senior in high school when she began restricting her eating after going on a summer trip abroad with a few friends. She had two older sisters in college who regaled her with tales of "freshman 15," cautioning her against that when she began her freshman year at college the following fall. Stella's mother was a stay-at-home parent, and her father was a veterinarian. Stella's mother first noticed the changes in her eating habits. Stella's initial stance was that she was eating the way she saw "Europeans ate" on her trip abroad. Stella's father shared in her mother's concern, and when Stella stopped getting her period, her parents made an appointment with the pediatrician to assess her overall health. The pediatrician recommended that the parents make an appointment as soon as possible with an FBT clinician, highlighting the urgency to get Stella's health back on track during her senior year, before she left for college in the fall. The pediatrician also stated that Stella's heart rate and blood pressure were borderline for medical hospitalization and emphasized that they needed to act quickly. Stella's parents were resolute in their desire to help get her back on track and read about FBT while waiting for their initial appointment. Stella was dismayed at receiving FBT and did not participate in the initial sessions, slumping moodily in her chair and refusing to make eye contact with anyone in the room. However, as the family progressed through phase 1, Stella began to push back less at meals and looked "resigned" as her parents described it, making her way through what they plated. She also began to come out of her shell more during sessions, particularly during one-on-one times with the therapist at the beginning of sessions. Additionally, Stella was gaining weight at a consistent pace, and both parents and therapist noted that her weight progress along with the behavioral changes such as asking for more to eat and expressing that she was hungry reflected readiness for phase 2 of FBT. Stella was eager to get back control over her eating, and progressed well through phase 2 initially, continuing to make appropriate weight progress and demonstrating the ability to make choices around what to pack for lunch. However, after spring break when Stella went to visit her older sister at college, her parents noticed some regression in her progress. Her weight began to decline slightly, and they noticed that she was making "healthier" choices when packing her lunch—omitting carbohydrates and replacing a cookie with an apple. Stella denied these changes when her parents discussed this with her, stating that she felt she had gotten to a healthy place, and look how far she had come since the beginning of treatment. Parents could not deny that she had made substantial progress and that she was indeed at a much better weight since she had started treatment. While she still had about 5 pounds to go, her father thought that she was at a good enough place, while her mother wondered if they should continue to push. Both parents felt exhausted after having gone through phase 1 and much of phase 2 and felt a little stuck at this last hurdle. They did not like to see Stella in distress again and felt conflicted in the face of all the progress she had made. They decided to take this challenge to her therapist.

This situation is a classic example of parents close to stumbling at the last hurdle and wanting to stop too soon. Stella *had* made undeniable progress, but a few other clues were beginning to ring the warning bells in her parents' heads. For instance, the stalling of progress appeared to happen after Stella visited her sister, and perhaps for the first time, had full control over her eating for the week at a college cafeteria. As Stella approached recovery, she appeared to be stuck on the last five pounds of her weight progress, digging in her heels and stating that how far she had come should be "good enough." She appeared to be making some small but potentially serious changes to her meals to try to stall her weight gain. Altogether, her parents were right to be concerned, even though Stella had done so well so far. They were not out of the woods—not quite yet.

In treatment sessions, Stella's therapist validated the warning bells the parents brought up. She encouraged them to think about whether or not Stella would feel this upset about making gains for her health before the eating disorder onset, or whether this seemed more driven by worries about her weight. The therapist reassured her parents that they had already done the hard work of phase 1 and had the skills to help Stella through these eating concerns that were re-emerging even after having made so much progress. Stella's perspective on how she could overcome these new worries was important at this stage to determine how decisively her parents had to step in. Stella admitted that during her spring break trip, she had been reminded of "freshman 15" and felt a little overwhelmed making all of her own meal choices at the school cafeteria. Her parents commended Stella for admitting these challenges and reminded her that until she left for college—and even after if need be—they were there to support her recovery. Together, they brainstormed getting back on track by reintegrating some of the foods Stella had been shying away from, with her parents planning to incorporate more of those into family dinners. It was not easy for Stella to overcome her worry about gaining the last few pounds, but with the concerted effort from her parents in restructuring boundaries around her eating and making sure requisite food groups were not eliminated, she was able to make her gains towards a full recovery.

This is a common example of a young person with AN doing quite well throughout treatment but struggling towards the end. In Stella's case, visiting a college campus for spring break and being reminded of her eating disorder thoughts was poorly timed to align with the last part of FBT. On the other hand, it may have been helpful for this "back sliding" to occur before she was at college without her parents to step in to help. Just approaching recovery weight can be enough to reinstate eating-disordered thoughts and behaviors in some young people. In these cases, it may be harder to notice a change. A good question to ask oneself in those moments of doubt is whether these arguments and pushback would be happening if the child was healthy. If not, it is likely that the pushback is not the healthy part of the child feeling bored with treatment or wanting to focus on other things in their life—rather, it is likely the worries are due to the eating-disordered thoughts reigniting.

How Falling at the Last Hurdle Interferes With FBT for Binge Eating and BN

Lee was a sophomore in high school when she began to engage in self-induced vomiting. She initially began skipping breakfast and lunch, citing having "forgotten" or "not having time." After school, her two fathers began noticing she would disappear upstairs with large family-sized bags of chips, and then would be "not hungry" for family dinners and pick at some of the options. She would also spend a long time in the bathroom after dinner saying she needed to shower and "self-care." Lee's younger brother heard her vomiting and brought it to their parents. When confronted, Lee said she was not feeling well. Worried, her parents brought Lee to her pediatrician. Her pediatrician was also concerned with both Lee's eating and purging behaviors and thought she would benefit from evaluation and treatment from an eating disorder specialist. Lee was diagnosed with Bulimia Nervosa and began FBT with her brother and her fathers. It became clear that Lee felt very ashamed and embarrassed about her binge eating and purging but did not know how to stop the behaviors. Lee's fathers were quickly able to put the appropriate supports in place, monitoring her eating and making sure Lee had three meals and regular snacks (to reduce the risk of binge eating) and would play a board game or watch a movie together after dinner to prevent purging episodes. While initially upset about these interventions, Lee eventually demonstrated a change in her behaviors. Towards the middle of phase 2, when Lee began to demonstrate more independence around managing her behaviors on her own without parent supervision or monitoring, her parents noticed Lee withdrawing from family dinners and seeming moodier during mealtimes. They also noticed her lunches coming back with parts uneaten. They spoke amongst themselves regarding whether or not this was cause for concern, and asked Lee outright if things were okay. Lee admitted that she had had a big fight with one of her closest friends around her upcoming high school graduation, and the stress that emerged from this social turmoil triggered a relapse. Lee began to restrict her intake initially in response to this uptick in stress, which lead to binge eating episodes in the evening. Further, Lee's pediatrician flagged concerns around re-emergence of purging behaviors. Lee ultimately revealed that she had started purging in the middle of the night to avoid parental scrutiny and engaging in secret exercise behaviors thereafter. Her parents were caught off guard and worried about this regression in behaviors, not sure how to intervene at this juncture.

Recurrence of binge eating and purging over the course of FBT for BN is to be expected, but less so over time. However, in this case, stressful events reignited Lee's weight-related anxieties and she was drawn back into binge eating and purging to try to manage them. While stressful and disappointing for her parents, these relapses can be an opportunity to be valuable learning experiences and consolidate the important gains Lee had made with her parents' help over the course of FBT. In this situation, Lee's parents had already begun to respond appropriately by probing the situation—both by asking Lee and having her assessed medically. In this case, it turned out their concerns were warranted, as Lee had relapsed and had begun to engage in previously sought out eating disorder behaviors.

Lee's parents and Lee discussed this "falling at the last hurdle" in their next FBT session. Lee's fathers were quite stuck in the "Why did this happen, what did we do wrong when things were going so well?" The therapist stated that in BN, it was not uncommon for a stressor to emerge and trigger a relapse. Here, it was important for the parents to remember their learning from phase 1 to act quickly and intervene during this relapse. Lee admitted that she felt quite anxious and out of control at night, thinking about her graduation, and noted that this was when her eating disorder thoughts were the loudest. The therapist encouraged the parents and Lee to jointly have a discussion to reset their progress. Lee and her parents identified that knowing her anxiety and tendency to engage in eating disorder behaviors got worse in the evening could be useful in making sure certain skills were put in place before she started to feel out of control. Lee herself was able to identify ways to make amends with her friend, to help her ride out the evening, and get back on track with her recovery efforts.

Lee's parents stepped in to help correct Lee's behaviors and get her back on track. While purging and exercising in the middle of the night was not something they had experienced in the initial stages of treatment, they relied on their skills and knowledge of how providing supportive interventions to prevent binge eating and purging were still helpful when applied at a later juncture in treatment. Moreover, Lee was able to be an active participant in this process by generating her own ideas and sharing what she was doing with less guilt and shame. At this stage of treatment, she was able to contribute to her recovery by identifying ways she might be able to intervene and manage her stress.

How Falling at the Last Hurdle Interferes With FBT for ARFID

Penny was a 7-year-old with ARFID and comorbid ADHD. She had always had some minor problems with being picky about the texture and temperature of food, but this did not significantly impact her growth until an incident when the family traveled abroad, and Penny got food poisoning after eating a chicken parmesan dish. Thereafter, Penny got very concerned with her food being "just the right tempera-ture" and started to eliminate cheese and meats. Her parents initially jokingly referred to her as their "Goldilocks" but began to get worried when they noticed a decline in her weight and growth, which was flagged by their pediatrician. They sought FBT for ARFID and made great gains initially using the "always, sometimes, never" list to guide food choices, implementing a reward system, and building upon past successes (chaining) to encourage Penny to re-integrate previously pre-ferred foods into her daily eating repertoire. Penny was motivated to a certain extent by the rewards she received but she was also pleased to be more a part of family meals because she had felt "left out" previ-ously. Despite her consistent and substantial progress, however, she still refused to eat chicken in any form. Her parents were happy with the progress she had made, and wondered if it was necessary to push Penny to try to add chicken to her diet. The work they had done was maybe good enough—her weight was back on track and her father reported feeling less like a short order cook. They did note, though, that chicken was often the main protein source for family dinners, and so Penny's reluctance to eat this did cause a considerable inconvenience. Her parents felt conflicted on how hard to push Penny to eat chicken, as they felt Penny's progress had been substantial so far and they were reluctant to re-engage in conflict and tantrums around meals for this "one last food."

Penny's ARFID appears to have been driven by anxiety around getting sick—or in other words—fear of aversive consequences from eating the chicken, as she experienced when her family went abroad. While her parents were correct that Penny had made substantial progress, if they chose to stop the progress here without adding back in chicken, they might inadvert-ently reinforce her fears about chicken. This would also mean continuing to burden the family with having to provide a substitute for a food they com-monly ate and also keep Penny on the sidelines of the family meal. This "last hurdle" for Penny might be one of the most important ones to get her back to her normal eating habits, given both the inclusion of chicken in family meals but also the messaging it might give to Penny's anxiety around food avoidance and getting sick. Her parents would likely have been remiss if they allowed her to continue avoiding chicken, rather than helping her overcome this fear that eating chicken means she would get sick.

In their next FBT session, the parents discussed their dilemma with the therapist. They also brought up their worry that if they insisted that Penny ate chicken, she might regress and start dropping off the foods they had worked so hard to include such as cheese and other meats. The therapist noted all the progress they had made so far and empathized with their reluctance to have ARFID-driven tantrums at mealtimes around adding chicken back in. She also noted the fear that pushing for this final food might result in some reluctance to have recently added back foods. The parents were understandably tired and had worked diligently with Penny to come this far. However, the therapist also highlighted the importance of mustering the energy and perseverance to push through this last obstacle. Penny eventually insisted on having chicken slathered in ketchup or barbeque sauce to mask the fact that it was chicken—but ate full plates of nuggets—much to her parents' relief! The therapist highlighted that this accomplishment not only made life easier for her parents—who could resume including chicken dishes in their weekly family dinners—but also showed Penny that she could eat and enjoy chicken and not get sick.

As these cases illustrate, across all types of eating disorders, it is important to persevere through to the very end of FBT. Not all families will face a "last hurdle"—but it is nevertheless important to keep eyes and ears peeled for any hints of relapsing or setbacks. It may be harder to notice, especially if the young person has been doing quite well for some time. However, as we see in the cases of Stella, Lee, and Penny, it is important listen to any warning bells, and step back in to provide help and support as needed with any relapses in behavior. As noted, these relapses can be an opportunity to gain further mastery over eating-disordered behaviors and can be viewed as a valuable part of recovery.

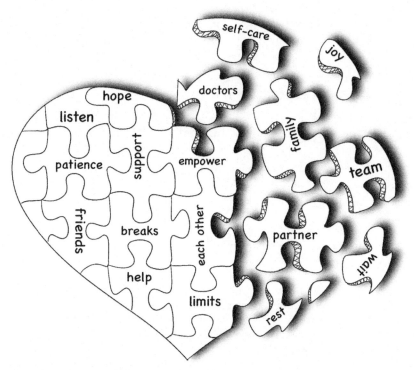

Figure 11.1 Find support: Why it is important for parents to seek support from professionals, families, friends, and organizations
Nandini Datta

11

Find Support: Why it is important for parents to seek support from professionals, families, friends, and organizations

I wish I had reached out to my close family and friends sooner. They had no idea how much we were struggling as a family, and it was so hard to

DOI: 10.4324/9781003353041-12

keep pretending that everything was okay. I felt like I was alone in a constant cloud of despair, panic, and worry. If the roles were reversed—and it was my friend's family going through this awful experience—I'd do anything possible to help them out. Not sure why I thought the same wouldn't hold true for me.

Mother of a young patient with BN

No Shame in the Support Game

One of the reasons parents may be hesitant to ask family members, friends, and their larger networks for support is that parents of children with eating disorders commonly feel shame or stigma about their child's mental health diagnosis. Thankfully, the stigma associated with mental health has decreased over time, though continues to be a significant barrier in seeking and receiving support.

To help families overcome their hesitancy to ask for support, we ask them to do the following exercise:

Imagine your child had a medical illness, like cancer. You likely would not hesitate to reach out to your extended networks for support to help your family manage during the course of your child's illness and treatment. Perhaps you would ask your neighbor to pick up your other children from school or soccer practice. Your youngest son's teacher would understand that you can no longer take on the task of the room parent volunteer that you signed up for before your child became ill. Friends might organize a meal train to help alleviate the stress of cooking. Or you might decide to hire extra supports to help manage the day-to-day tasks, like cleaning or laundry.

A child recovering from an eating disorder is no different from a child recovering from any serious illness. The extra burden, stress, time, and attention that now must be diverted to help a very sick child is enormous. Instead of avoiding support, seek it, seek it now, and seek it often. The saying "It's not a sprint, it's a marathon" is relevant here. To get to the finish line requires thinking about managing your energy and strength for the long haul—and that is more likely if there are supportive people around you to help.

The Struggle Is Real

As a parent of a child with an eating disorder, one of the most helpful things for the entire family to do is to seek support from others during this time. Reaching out for support can maximize one's ability to successfully combat a child's eating disorder. Yet this is one of those "easier said than done" tasks. First, parents must recognize when and where they need the support, and allow themselves to acknowledge that the burden of care associated with treating an eating disorder will be great. This is particularly true early in treatment. Demands on time and energy are highest at the beginning of FBT when parents are learning how best to help their child recover from an eating disorder and practicing new skills to encourage re-nourishment or block other problematic eating disorder behaviors. Learning something new is often hard, uncomfortable, and challenging, and it requires extra energy and brainpower. It may be especially hard to rest and recharge when there is so much worry about a child's physical health and mental well-being. During these times it is especially useful to utilize the individuals in one's network to provide support—whether that is tangible support or emotional encouragement.

For individuals battling the eating disorder with another parent or caregiver, it is especially important to be open and honest in communication about what is needed to be most successful in this fight. Partners often possess a different (and sometimes complementary) set of skills and strengths. Use this as an advantage in working together with treatment goals. At times, parents may find it helpful to tag team tasks or allow one parent to "tap out" for a meal in order to reset, particularly when emotions and stress are high. Or perhaps one partner can take on all the household chores if another partner is managing snack times for the child with the eating disorder. Remember to go back to Chapter 3 on alignment and working together for a deeper exploration of the reasons why alignment is crucial in helping children recover.

Avoiding Therapy Sessions

Occasionally families might feel like they are "failing" FBT if their child is not showing weight gain or other evidence of behavioral progress each week. This can lead to families avoiding therapy sessions due to shame or feelings of failure. Some families may even feel that something is wrong with them or that FBT is not the right treatment for them. FBT therapists are a great resource who can help problem-solve challenges and reconsider creative options if parents are feeling stuck, overwhelmed, or confused. Perhaps all it might take is setting smaller, more manageable goals each week that could result in slow yet steady progress towards recovery. FBT therapists are not there to judge or blame parents. Each family's journey is unique. FBT therapists are there to help families learn more about eating disorders and identify potential pitfalls that might arise as they navigate recovery together as a family. Therapists are essential team members in this fight.

The goal of the FBT therapist is to support parents in successfully completing a very difficult task. When things are not going well, the FBT therapist will join in the struggle to help identify what might be getting in the way of success. Their collective knowledge of helping many families (who may have experienced similar challenges!) can be an invaluable resource in collaborating together to find a solution that will work.

One important note regarding progress in FBT. If a child needs to gain weight as part of their eating disorder recovery, the review of weight and visual graphing on the chart each session is not intended to "shame" or "guilt trip" parents. Rather, when used correctly, this information serves as a data point to help guide the FBT session to focus on specific skills and strategies that are the most helpful. Remember—parents are not battling this alone. Working together with the FBT treatment team to identify these feelings and find solutions to move forward can make all the difference.

Ideas for Support Seekers

While every family is unique, here are a few ways to consider seeking support if feeling overwhelmed, burnt out, or exhausted. One tip – consider seeking support early on in the process – before you become overly fatigued.

This is just a small list of potential ideas to consider when needing additional support through this process. The FBT therapist can also help problem-solve each unique family situation and suggest additional ways to seek out support that can make all the difference between moving forward, staying stuck, or feeling defeated in the fight against a child's eating disorder. Eating disorders do not take a holiday, and neither can parents but they can take a break for a bit. Taking care of themselves ultimately allows parents to take better care of their children. As discussed throughout this book, eating disorders are challenging and the worries they incite in parents of children afflicted with them can be difficult to quell. The behaviors and thinking patterns associated with an eating disorder *do not* have a child's best interest at heart. Parents do. The saying "it takes a village" in regards to raising a child applies here too—it is worth the time investment to figure out who and what may be in this "village" and how these resources can be most helpful. Parents may need to think creatively to find solutions that will work the best for themselves and their family. There may not be a "one size fits all" approach when it comes to support.

Table 11.1 Ideas for Seeking Support

- Redistribute household tasks.
- Ask neighbors/friends/family members to help with school pick-up/drop-off.
- Find carpools for afterschool activities.
- Coordinate with the child's school for accommodations.
- Reprioritize household tasks. (For example, does the bathroom really need cleaning this week? Can the dusting wait? Does the laundry have to be put away *right now?*)
- Call a trusted friend.
- Video-chat with a family member who lives far away.
- Schedule an outing with a friend.
- Intentionally reconnect with partner.
- Take a nap.
- Video-call a support person during meal/snack time for extra support and/or distraction.
- Attend a support group or participate in an online parent forum.
- Have family or friends visit for an extended period of time to provide extra help.
- Identify the "burnout" tipping point and come up with a system to "tap out" when needed.
- Use a meal delivery service or order takeout food, if funding allows.
- Consider if any activities or events can be dropped, postponed, or removed from the schedule (or the child's schedule).
- Ask others explicitly for help—many people want to help in a crisis, but may just not know how. Do not be afraid to tell them exactly what would be helpful ("It would be great if you could pick up Johnny from ballet" or "I really need a bag of sugar and a few eggs—can you pick those up from the store?").
- Connect with others through a religious group or organization.
- Consider if taking a leave of absence from work is needed; it may be possible to take partial leave or work out a plan with employers to protect time away from work for medical/therapy appointments and/or time to supervise lunch.
- Schedule time each week to communicate with partner/support team about support and what changes are needed to feel more supported.
- Seek out mental health support services.

In addition to support from family and friends, there are parent groups that may be helpful for some parents to explore. Families Empowered and Supporting Treatment for Eating Disorders (FEAST: www.feast-ed.org) is an organization that has educational events and parent support groups that may be useful for some parents. The National Eating Disorders Association

(NEDA) and BEAT, a parent-run organization in the UK, are two other groups that parents might find helpful to find support.

Seeking Support in AN

Shelley and Kevin were parents to Tristian, a 14-year-old boy with AN. Tristian had started restricting his food intake over the past year, avoiding all foods other than fruits, vegetables, and lean meats. He was also engaging in one to two hours of exercise per day. As a result, Tristian had lost significant weight and was experiencing medical complications from the restriction and over-exercise. Shelley and Kevin acted quickly once they realized what was happening. The family started FBT and began monitoring all of Tristian's meals and snacks. Tristian had a hard time increasing his intake and being asked to eat foods that he feared would "make him fat." His parents reported that most meals resulted in Tristian screaming, cursing at them, and even throwing food at times. Meals would often last for an hour or longer. By the end of the first month, Shelley and Kevin reported feeling exhausted, overwhelmed, and burnt out. They shared these feelings with their FBT therapist, who helped Tristian's parents identify strategies to decrease burnout and exhaustion. The therapist suggested the parents consider setting time limits for meals and coming up with a signal that would alert the other parent to when one parent needed to step away from the meal to re-center themselves. Together with consultation from the therapist, Tristian's parents decided that one parent would prepare the meals/snacks while the other parent would be responsible for clean-up. The therapist also highlighted the need for Tristian's parents to reset and recharge after particularly stressful mealtimes. Shelley decided that she would take the 30 minutes after dinner to engage in calming, pleasant activities (like taking a bath, reading a book, going for a solo walk) while Kevin managed dinner clean-up and other family responsibilities. Likewise, the family decided that Shelley would be primarily responsible for weekend breakfast time while Kevin slept in or went for a run.

After just one week of implementing the new plan, Tristian's parents reported feeling more refreshed, less stressed, and better able to work together as a parent team in fighting Tristian's eating disorder. While these new strategies did not alleviate all the stressors—their child's health was still in danger and each meal/snack was an important step in the right direction—identifying when and in what ways Tristian's parents needed extra support allowed them to feel more confident in tackling this hard yet vitally important task.

Seeking Support in BN

Rodrigo was a 16-year-old boy recently diagnosed with BN. He lived at home with his mother Maria and twin 13-year-old sisters. One of Rodrigo's treatment targets was to stop purging (vomiting). Rodrigo tended to purge when he felt like he had overeaten, which usually happened after his snack when he got home from school. This was typically a time when Rodrigo was home alone, as his mother was busy taking his sisters to dance practice. Maria was a single mother without close extended family living nearby. In order to help provide monitoring and support for Rodrigo to prevent purging during this high-risk time, Maria arranged for another parent in her daughter's dance class to bring the girls home from practice while she stayed with Rodrigo in the afternoons. This allowed Maria to provide extra support to Rodrigo during his afterschool snack and helped disrupt the binge eating/purge cycle of his eating disorder.

Although this example may seem very simple and straightforward, it is not unusual for parents to struggle with asking for even these minimal requests for support. Keep this example in mind if you're a parent who tends to want to be totally self-sufficient. Help is usually there when it's asked for.

Seeking Support in ARFID

Betzy, a 7-year-old with ARFID, lived with her married parents and 11-year-old brother. Since she was an infant, Betzy had never shown a strong interest in food or eating. Betzy reported that she was just "not interested" in food and would "forget" to eat. Her ARFID presentation most closely aligned with low interest and low appetite subtype. Betzy had a hard time sitting at the table during mealtimes and would often take one or two bites of her meal before declaring that she was full and did not want any more to eat. Mealtimes became quite stressful, as Betzy's parents worried about her nutrition and growth. This resulted in conflict, arguments, pleading, and even yelling in an effort to get Betzy to eat more foods. The family was able to identify feeling "burnt out" and "exhausted" from asking Betzy to eat new foods and her near constant refusals. Betzy's mother Angelina explained to the FBT therapist just how exhausting it was to "beg" Betzy to eat every day. Angelina also suspected this was negatively impacting her relationship with Betzy, as frustrations around not eating carried over beyond the dinner table. The FBT therapist asked the family if they could think of any strategies that might help provide more support for Betzy's parents while also making mealtimes less stressful. The family noted that Betzy seemed happier and calmer at mealtimes when they ate together with Betzy's maternal grandmother, who lived about 30 minutes away. Betzy was very close with her maternal grandmother and had shared a special, supportive bond ever since she was young. The family had stopped going to visit and were declining social events with extended family due to how stressful it was to ensure Betzy was eating during these occasions. After some discussion around potential ideas, the family decided to ask Betzy's grandmother to come over for dinner twice a week. Betzy began looking forward to these special dinners and the whole family enjoyed a more calm, relaxed evening. Betzy was able to share that it was "easier to eat more" when her grandmother was around because "dinner is more fun" and "everyone is less mad." Betzy's grandmother was happy to help support and equally looked forward to these special times with her grandchildren. The enjoyment and novelty of having another family member join them for dinner allowed Betzy and her parents to be more successful in increasing Betzy's food intake while also creating a calmer, more enjoyable eating environment. Having Betzy's grandmother provide support for Betzy during treatment also allowed the family to feel more comfortable attending social gatherings and events with extended family, which helped improve everyone's mood and decrease feelings of loneliness and isolation.

While Tristian, Rodrigo, and Betzy's situations were all unique, each family benefited from figuring out a way to seek out and accept support to better assist them in challenging their child's eating disorder. This extra support ultimately allowed them to make faster and more significant progress in their child's recovery from an eating disorder. Support might come from conversations with spouses or partners, as in Tristian's case, to perhaps a realignment of household priorities and providing much-needed breaks to reset and recharge. Rodrigo's mother Maria found creative solutions to make sure the needs of all her children were being met, asking others to provide transportation for her daughters so that she could support Rodrigo when he needed it most. Extended family and close friends are often a very helpful source of support, as reflected in Betzy's case. Remember—an eating disorder affects everyone in the family. Be sure to consistently evaluate and re-evaluate when, how, and in what ways all family members can most benefit from additional support. The journey may be long and grueling, but families do not have to go it alone!

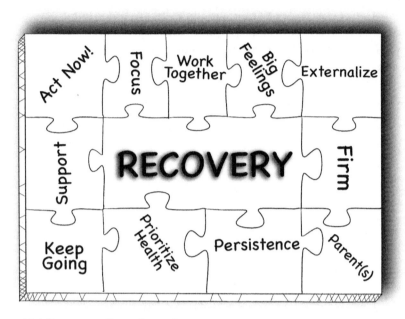

Figure 12.1 Bringing it all together and moving on
Nandini Datta

12

Bringing It All together and Moving On

Sometimes it takes some time to really listen and learn… We think we understand and it all makes sense, but then it seems to slip away and it seems we learn a little more as we are able to take in more, bit by bit…
    Parent talking to FBT therapist about taking in her suggestions

Putting the Pieces Together

Learning how to help a child with an eating disorder is not easy. It is confusing, perplexing, exhausting, and at times a bit depressing for some. That's

DOI: 10.4324/9781003353041-13

in part because for most parents it is extremely unfamiliar territory, so there's a lot to try to get a handle on. As a result, it is not surprising—as with all learning—that there are challenges and setbacks in the process. This book endeavors to help parents understand the most common challenges that we have seen in our experience helping families in FBT. Here is a list of the key pieces that need to come together to make FBT work:

1. **Don't wait**: Hesitation is a friend to the eating disorder; it allows the behaviors and thoughts to become more entrenched and harder to change, so act now!

2. **Don't worry about why**: Focusing on what caused the eating disorder is not useful when the cognition, emotions, and behaviors are dragging down a child's health and well-being.

3. **Work together**: Parenting is usually a team sport and to be successful parents and families need to find a way to overcome differences about how to help their child.

4. **Emotions will sometimes run high**: It is very difficult for caring parents to see their children suffer—as it should be—but an eating disorder often exacerbates and magnifies feelings in order to keep parents from taking necessary steps to stop destructive eating-disordered behaviors.

5. **Eating disorders are not rational**: It is hard for parents to appreciate that their child is not thinking clearly when they have an eating disorder and many hope they can reason with them, but this seldom works and instead leads to endless circular debates and frustration, so don't try to reason with eating-disordered thinking. As the child gets better, the ability to engage them in helping themselves will increase.

6. **Insight is not enough**: Understanding a problem is not the same as overcoming it. A child with an eating disorder will need to actually change eating patterns and behaviors and will need their parents to help them do this.

7. **Make efforts pay off**: Sometimes it seems that compromise and negotiation for small changes are easier and will lead to bigger changes, but with eating disorders, this often means the child remains trapped in the eating disorder, so make changes that matter, not ones that only chip away at the edges.

8. **Keep focused**: Life is complex and endlessly full of challenges and it is tempting to drift away from difficult problems or focus on other things, but when a child has an eating disorder, it is imperative to keep focused and on point.

9. **Don't stop until you reach the top**: It is hard work to help a child over-come an eating disorder and it is tempting to be comforted with some progress and hope for the best, but this can too often backfire and lead to relapse.

10. **Don't go it alone**: As with any illness, parents with a sick child need support from others, and need to find ways to support themselves.

But How Do These Pieces Fit Together to Complete the Puzzle?

The first piece is the keystone—as soon as parents are aware that their child is developing an eating disorder or has been diagnosed, they should get started right away. We know that early effective intervention is the best hope for preventing enduring illness and minimizing immediate and long-term harms. This piece connects to focusing on changing the maintaining behaviors rather than trying to figure out exactly how and why a child has developed an eating disorder. Spending weeks and months trying to determine possible causes leads to a delay in actually changing the behaviors. Delaying like this can be harmful and lead to behaviors and worries about eating and weight becoming increasingly entrenched and harder to modify. To be effective in changing these destructive behaviors, it is necessary to make sure the next puzzle piece—working together as parents and family—is in place to develop a consistent, persistent, and caring approach that all agree to and support each other in making sure it is applied.

Don't expect it to be easy when starting out in FBT. It is challenging for any parent to tolerate distress and emotional outbursts and to accept that reasoning doesn't work with the irrational thoughts and feelings that accom-pany eating disorders. While a child may understand much about their eating disorder, the proof is in the real change in behaviors—under-eating, binge eating, purging, excessive exercise, fearful eating, highly selective eating—that keep the eating disorder in place. Accepting this means that—for a time—many other aspects of ordinary life must be reorganized and parents must focus on changing these eating-disordered behaviors. This is challen-ging because of the impact such reorganization has on all members of the family, on everyday routines, especially mealtimes, and on parental work and social lives. For these reasons, it is important to make these efforts "pay off" and be as efficient and effective as possible to minimize the impacts of this necessary focus on family and personal lives. Trying to go slow or giving breaks to behavioral interventions diminishes their effectiveness and threatens the ultimate goal of recovery from the eating disorder. With children and adolescents with eating disorders there is a very real chance at obtaining lasting recovery so aiming high for this goal is a piece of the puzzle that parents should aspire to in their efforts.

Eating disorders are stigmatized illnesses and this unfortunate truth is only very slowly changing. This means that many families feel ashamed and aim to hide the eating disorder from family and friends, leading to isolation and sometimes depression. So, the last puzzle piece—seeking support—from family, friends, and other professionals—will help to keep parents and families energized and productive and results in a greater chance of being effective in helping their children overcome their eating disorder.

About Hope

We hope that this book with its focus on common dilemmas parents struggle with in FBT will help parents and families be more effective in helping their children overcome their eating disorder. We hope the illustrations from multiple families facing the full range of eating problems will help parents see themselves and some of their own worries, hesitancies, and concerns in some of them. Of course we also hope that how the families learned, developed, and changed as they better appreciated what they needed to do will help all parents move forward in their thinking and plans for helping their child. We have ourselves learned so much from families over the many years we have been helping them using FBT and their wisdom is really what we hope parents will use as they help their children with their eating disorder. We don't always have to re-invent the wheel, though of course we do all need to learn how particular knowledge or strategies might need to be adapted and modified in a specific family and that will be up to parents and an FBT therapist to think through together.

We like to remind both professionals and families that at its core, psychotherapy of all types is a form of learning—sometimes the focus is on one type or another—but the goal of psychotherapy is to promote change through learning whether it be about behaviors, emotions, cognitions, or social processes. This is certainly the case with FBT. From the start, therapists aim to help parents and families learn about eating disorders, understand how their child and family is affected, and develop and implement an approach to overcoming the eating disorder that will work for their family.

So our final hope is that this book will help parents with their learning as they work with FBT therapists to help their child overcome their eating disorder, which leads to lasting recovery and helps children and families continue to grow and develop without an eating disorder further interfering or disrupting the joyful progress of family life.

Resources

Review of Scientific Support

Datta, N., Matheson, B., Citron, K., Van Wye E.M., & Lock, J.D. (2023) Evidence Based Update on Psychosocial Treatments for Eating Disorders in Children and Adolescents, *Journal of Clinical Child & Adolescent Psychology*, 52:2, 159–170, DOI: 10.1080/15374416.2022.2109650

Books

Bryant-Waugh, R. (2020) *Avoidant Restrictive Food Intake Disorder: A Guide for Parents and Carers*. New York, New York: Routledge.

Le Grange, D., Lock, J. (2007) *Treatment Manual for Bulimia Nervosa: A Family-Based Approach*. New York, New York: Guilford Press.

Lock, J. (2022) *Family-Based Treatment for Avoidant/Restrictive Food Intake Disorder*. New York, New York: Routledge.

Lock, J., LeGrange, D. (2015) *Help Your Teenager Beat an Eating Disorder*. New York, New York: Guilford Press.

Lock, J., Le Grange, D., Agras, S., & Dare, C. (2013) *Treatment Manual for Anorexia Nervosa: A Family-Based Approach*, Second Edition. New York, New York: Guilford.

Websites

Anorexia Family: www.anorexiafamily.com/

BEAT: www.beateatingdisorders.org.uk/

FEAST: www.feast-ed.org/

NEDA: www.nationaleatingdisorders.org/

Index

Printed in Great Britain
by Amazon

56365772R00097